K–8 Diagnostic Assessment

Overview

The purpose of this book is to help you manage the use of multiple assessments, interpret the results, and then use that information for instructional planning. It will provide you with basic definitions and clear guidance on how test scores can be a useful resource for addressing your students' needs.

What is assessment?

- Assessment is the process of systematically gathering evidence about what students know and can do.
- Assessments can be both formal and informal as long as the information is systematically collected, scored, and recorded.

Types of assessment

Diagnostic Assessments can be used for screening or placement. They can also be used for formative or summative assessment. A diagnostic test:

- Is a test administered to those students who appear at risk of failing to read, or need additional instruction.
- Is a detailed assessment that pinpoints a student's strengths or weaknesses.
- Is a test that can be group or individually administered, depending on the test and the age of the student.
- Should be given near the beginning of the year to determine students' instructional needs or whenever a student is suspected of having difficulty learning taught skills. It may also be given throughout the year to monitor student progress (e.g., Fluency Assessment).
- Can be used to form skills-based small groups.

Screening/Placement Assessments provide overall information about the skill base of a student. A screening test:

- Is useful for determining the most appropriate starting point for instruction and for planning instruction.
- Usually includes formal and informal measures with clear mastery targets.
- Provides more general information, such as the student reads below grade level. Whereas, a diagnostic assessment will help you target specific skill deficiencies, such as decoding words with long vowel spellings.

K–8 Diagnostic Assessment

Progress Monitoring Assessments are ongoing and provide up-to-date information on a student's mastery of taught skills. A progress monitoring assessment:

- Is also known as a Formative Assessment.
- Includes teacher observations (Quick Checks), weekly and unit tests, and curriculum assignments.
- Mirrors the types of tasks students complete in the curriculum (curriculum-based).
- May include a diagnostic assessment that pinpoints the cause of a specific observed reading problem.
- Helps to define the specific focus on instruction (e.g., reteaching a skill students haven't mastered).

Summative Assessments are administered at the end of a major unit of study such as at the end of a semester or school year. A summative assessment:

- Provides information about what skills a student exits the major instructional period with.
- Is useful for planning the next major instructional period.
- Is connected to the specific curriculum.
- Can be used to provide a final grade or judgment on a student's strengths and weaknesses.

Using Multiple Measures

The Assessment Process

The assessment process is making instructional decisions based on assessment information.

- All decisions should be based on “multiple measures” or more than one kind of assessment or set of scores.
- The process starts with collecting assessment evidence (test results, observations).
- The next step is to compare and interpret the information you have gathered.
- The third step is to make instructional decisions based on your conclusions.
- This process is ongoing: collect evidence, interpret, make decisions. . . .

The Assessment Process

Collect and review
Assessment Evidence.
Use multiple sources of evidence (test scores, observations).

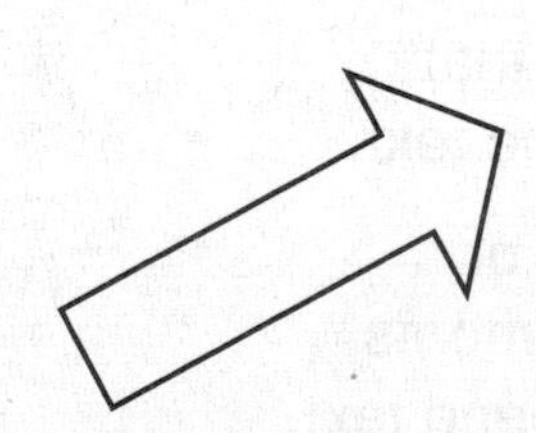

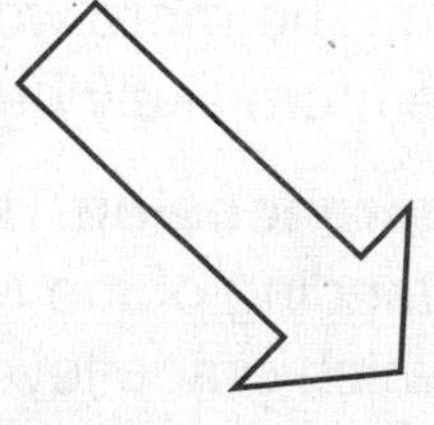

Make
Instructional Decisions
based on the conclusions you have drawn.

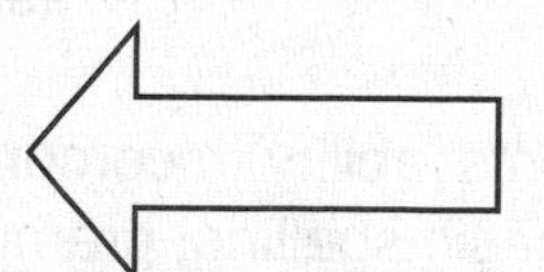

Decide what the evidence
Means.
Compare and contrast scores and observations with other assessment results.

Diagnostic Assessments

This book includes the following diagnostic assessments:

- **Phonemic Awareness** Students who struggle with decoding often lack the ability to perceive and manipulate sounds (phonemes) in spoken words. Phonemic Awareness strongly correlates to early reading growth and is a key skill to assess with beginning readers.
- **Phonics and Decoding** Basic decoding proficiency and mastery of sound-spelling relationships is necessary for reading success. Decoding proficiency can be assessed using lists of real and pseudowords.
- **Oral Reading Fluency** The hallmark of a skilled reader is one who can decode and comprehend simultaneously. Oral reading fluency assessments determine which students are above, on, or below level for reading grade-level text. Oral reading fluency assessments correlate strongly to standardized comprehension assessments and are a quick measure to determine students' overall reading proficiency. These assessments can also be used to monitor the effect of instructional modifications or interventions as they are very sensitive to reading growth.
- **Spelling** Spelling ability supports fluent reading and writing. Students use their knowledge of spelling patterns when reading and writing.
- **Vocabulary** Vocabulary knowledge is also highly correlated to comprehension. The more words a student knows and the deeper that knowledge, the more likely he or she will be able to comprehend the text.
- **Reading Comprehension** The goal of reading is comprehension, or overall understanding of the text. Reading Comprehension assessments determine at which grade level students can successfully comprehend text. These assessments are useful for providing leveled practice materials and serve as a starting point for instruction as you move struggling students to grade-level proficiency.
- **Writing** Writing is a reflection of students' ability to comprehend ideas, express thoughts, and master basic spelling, grammar, usage, and mechanics skills. Assessing writing needs can help the teacher individualize instruction and accelerate student progress.

K–8 Diagnostic Assessment

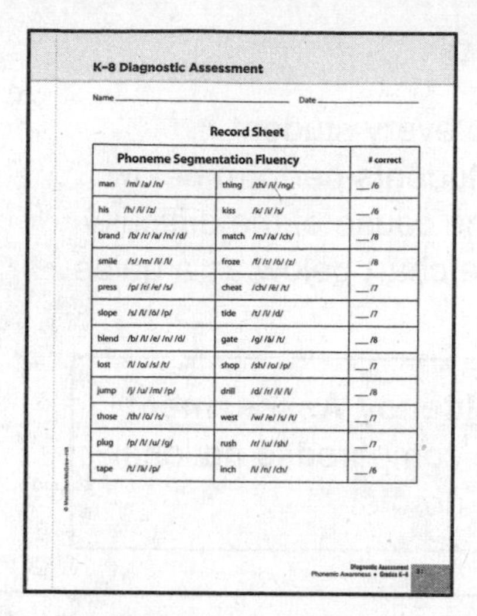

K–8 Diagnostic Assessment

Name ______________________ Date ____________

Record Sheet

Phoneme Segmentation Fluency				# correct
man	/m/ /a/ /n/	thing	/th/ /i/ /ng/	__/6
his	/h/ /i/ /z/	kiss	/k/ /i/ /s/	__/6
brand	/b/ /r/ /a/ /n/ /d/	match	/m/ /a/ /ch/	__/8
smile	/s/ /m/ /ī/ /l/	froze	/f/ /r/ /ō/ /z/	__/8
press	/p/ /r/ /e/ /s/	cheat	/ch/ /ē/ /t/	__/7
slope	/s/ /l/ /ō/ /p/	tide	/t/ /ī/ /d/	__/7
blend	/b/ /l/ /e/ /n/ /d/	gate	/g/ /ā/ /t/	__/8
lost	/l/ /o/ /s/ /t/	shop	/sh/ /o/ /p/	__/7
jump	/j/ /u/ /m/ /p/	drill	/d/ /r/ /i/ /l/	__/8
those	/th/ /ō/ /s/	west	/w/ /e/ /s/ /t/	__/7
plug	/p/ /l/ /u/ /g/	rush	/r/ /u/ /sh/	__/7
tape	/t/ /ā/ /p/	inch	/i/ /n/ /ch/	__/6

Phonemic Awareness

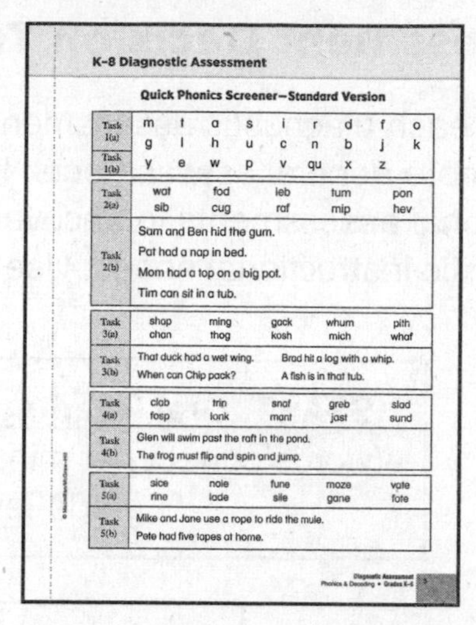

K–8 Diagnostic Assessment

Quick Phonics Screener—Standard Version

Task	
Task 1(a)	m t a s i r d f o g l h u c n b j k
Task 1(b)	y e w p v qu x z
Task 2(a)	wat fod leb tum pon sib cug raf mip hev
Task 2(b)	Sam and Ben hid the gum. Pat had a nap in bed. Mom had a top on a big pot. Tim can sit in a tub.
Task 3(a)	shap ming gack whum pith chan thog kosh mich whaf
Task 3(b)	That duck had a wet wing. Brad hit a log with a whip. When can Chip pack? A fish is in that tub.
Task 4(a)	clab trin snaf greb slad fosp lonk mant jast sund
Task 4(b)	Glen will swim past the raft in the pond. The frog must flip and spin and jump.
Task 5(a)	sice noie fune moze vate rine lade sile gane fote
Task 5(b)	Mike and Jane use a rope to ride the mule. Pete had five lopes at home.

Phonics and Decoding

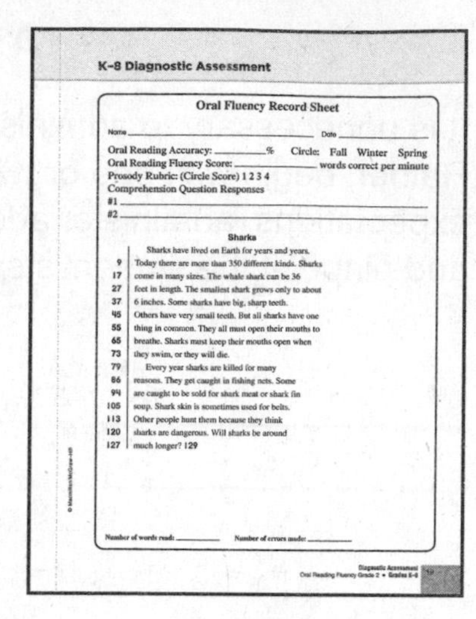

K–8 Diagnostic Assessment

Oral Fluency Record Sheet

Name ______________________ Date ____________

Oral Reading Accuracy: ________% Circle: Fall Winter Spring

Oral Reading Fluency Score: ____________ words correct per minute

Prosody Rubric: (Circle Score) 1 2 3 4

Comprehension Question Responses

#1 ______________________

#2 ______________________

Sharks

	Sharks have lived on Earth for years and years.
9	Today there are more than 350 different kinds. Sharks
17	come in many sizes. The whale shark can be 36
27	feet in length. The smallest shark grows only to about
37	6 inches. Some sharks have big, sharp teeth.
45	Others have very small teeth. But all sharks have one
55	thing in common. They all must open their mouths to
65	breathe. Sharks must keep their mouths open when
73	they swim, or they will die.
79	Every year sharks are killed for many
86	reasons. They get caught in fishing nets. Some
94	are caught to be sold for shark meat or shark fin
105	soup. Shark skin is sometimes used for belts.
113	Other people hunt them because they think
120	sharks are dangerous. Will sharks be around
127	much longer? 129

Number of words read: ________ Number of errors made: ________

Fluency

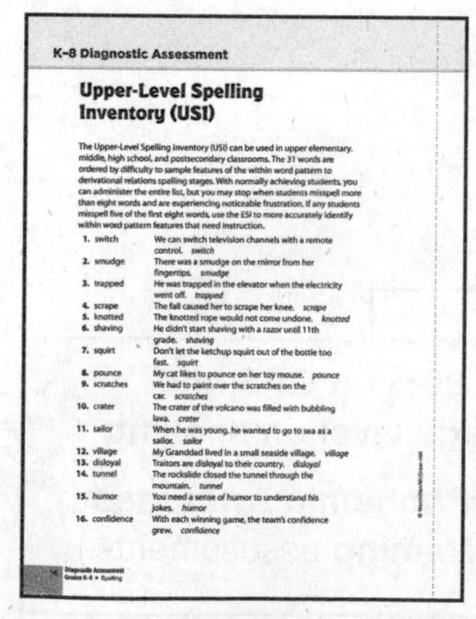

K–8 Diagnostic Assessment

Upper-Level Spelling Inventory (USI)

The Upper-Level Spelling Inventory (USI) can be used in upper elementary, middle, high school, and postsecondary classrooms. The 31 words are ordered by difficulty to sample features of the within word pattern to derivational relations spelling stages. With normally achieving students, you can administer the entire list, but you may stop when students misspell more than eight words and are experiencing noticeable frustration. If any students misspell five of the first eight words, use the ESI to more accurately identify within word pattern features that need instruction.

1. switch — We can switch television channels with a remote control. *switch*
2. smudge — There was a smudge on the mirror from her fingertips. *smudge*
3. trapped — He was trapped in the elevator when the electricity went off. *trapped*
4. scrape — The fall caused her to scrape her knee. *scrape*
5. knotted — The knotted rope would not come undone. *knotted*
6. shaving — He didn't start shaving with a razor until 11th grade. *shaving*
7. squirt — Don't let the ketchup squirt out of the bottle too fast. *squirt*
8. pounce — My cat likes to pounce on her toy mouse. *pounce*
9. scratches — We had to paint over the scratches on the car. *scratches*
10. crater — The crater of the volcano was filled with bubbling lava. *crater*
11. sailor — When he was young, he wanted to go to sea as a sailor. *sailor*
12. village — My Granddad lived in a small seaside village. *village*
13. disloyal — Traitors are disloyal to their country. *disloyal*
14. tunnel — The rockslide closed the tunnel through the mountain. *tunnel*
15. humor — You need a sense of humor to understand his jokes. *humor*
16. confidence — With each winning game, the team's confidence grew. *confidence*

Spelling

K–8 Diagnostic Assessment

Critchlow Verbal Language Scale

Name: ______________ Grade: ________ Date: ________

Directions: Ask the student to say the opposite of each word. Discontinue testing after five consecutive errors.

	STIMULUS	RESPONSE		STIMULUS	RESPONSE
____	1. boy	girl	____	39. multiply	divide
____	2. up	down	____	40. friend	enemy
____	3. front	back	____	41. difficult	easy
____	4. hot	cold	____	42. narrow	wide
____	5. brother	sister	____	43. wild	tame
____	6. dirty	clean	____	44. dangerous	safe
____	7. wet	dry	____	45. entrance	exit
____	8. crooked	straight	____	46. sharp	dull
____	9. young	old	____	47. imprisoned	free
____	10. off	on	____	48. falsehood	truth
____	11. shut	open	____	49. public	private
____	12. noisy	quiet	____	50. costly	cheap
____	13. dead	alive	____	51. lengthen	shorten
____	14. early	late	____	52. succeed	fail
____	15. empty	full	____	53. victory	defeat
____	16. near	far	____	54. stale	fresh
____	17. come	go	____	55. timid	bold-brave
____	18. north	south	____	56. maximum	minimum
____	19. lost	found	____	57. unite	separate
____	20. pretty	ugly-homely	____	58. profit	loss
____	21. sick	well	____	59. complex	simple
____	22. sour	sweet	____	60. create	destroy
____	23. add	subtract	____	61. vertical	horizontal
____	24. daughter	son	____	62. former	latter
____	25. remember	forget	____	63. bless	curse
____	26. false	true	____	64. loiter	hurry
____	27. love	hate	____	65. discord	harmony
____	28. heavy	light	____	66. gradual	sudden
____	29. tight	loose	____	67. diminish	increase
____	30. after	before	____	68. naive	sophisticated
____	31. laugh	cry	____	69. superfluous	necessary
____	32. smooth	rough	____	70. asset	liability
____	33. absent	present-here	____	71. tentative	permanent
____	34. strong	weak	____	72. clergy	laity
____	35. evening	morning	____	73. corpulent	slender
____	36. raw	cooked	____	74. epilogue	prologue
____	37. begin	end-stop	____	75. autocracy	democracy
____	38. same	different			

Score: ________ /75

Vocabulary

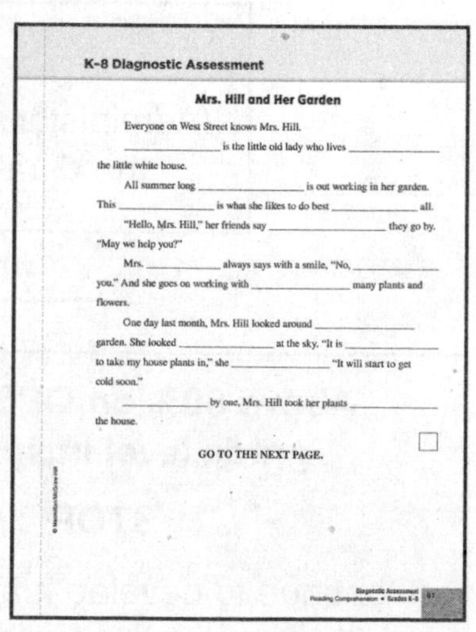

K–8 Diagnostic Assessment

Mrs. Hill and Her Garden

Everyone on West Street knows Mrs. Hill.

__________ is the little old lady who lives __________ the little white house.

All summer long __________ is out working in her garden. This __________ is what she likes to do best __________ all.

"Hello, Mrs. Hill," her friends say __________ they go by. "May we help you?"

Mrs. __________ always says with a smile, "No, __________ you." And she goes on working with __________ many plants and flowers.

One day last month, Mrs. Hill looked around __________ garden. She looked __________ at the sky. "It is __________ to take my house plants in," she __________ "It will start to get cold soon."

__________ by one, Mrs. Hill took her plants __________ the house.

GO TO THE NEXT PAGE.

Reading Comprehension

Assessment Decision Tree

It is unnecessary to administer each diagnostic assessment to every student. Rather, begin with one or two more general assessments. If students perform below expectations, administer additional assessments to uncover the cause of the difficulty and pinpoint the student's specific instructional needs. Use the chart below as a guide.

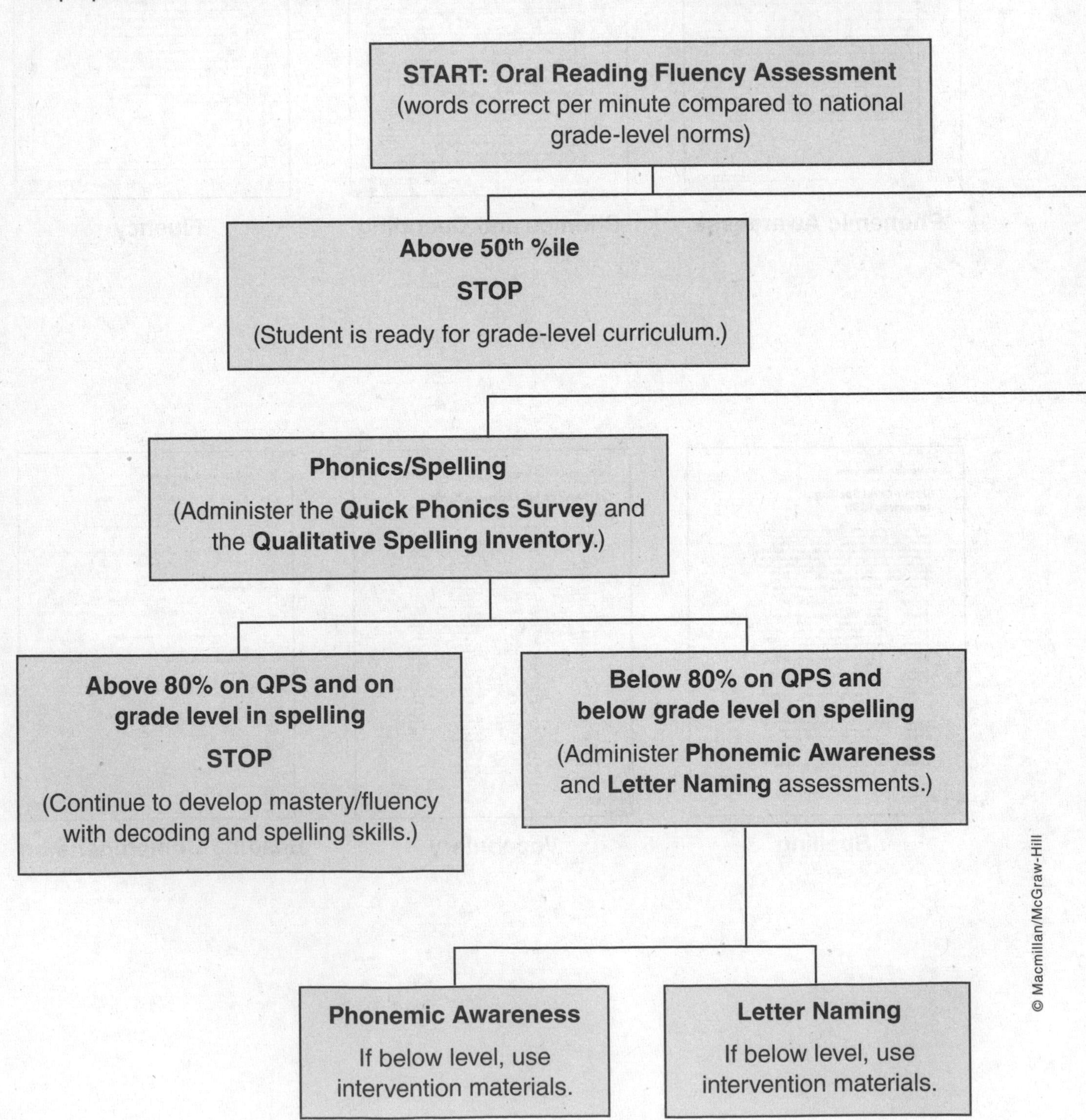

K–8 Diagnostic Assessment

Below 50th %ile
(Administer additional assessments to determine underlying skill needs.)

Comprehension
(Administer the **Leveled Passages Assessment** and the **Metacomprehension Strategy Index**.)

- **On or Above grade level**
  STOP
  (Continue to monitor students during whole group and small group instruction.)
- **Below grade level**
  (Consider placement in intervention materials. Use small group instructional time to preteach skills and rebuild foundational skill needs.)

Vocabulary
(Administer the **Critchlow Verbal Language Scale** and **Sight Word Fluency Assessment**.)

- **On or above grade level**
  STOP
  (Continue to work with students on weekly vocabulary during small group time.)
- **Below grade level**
  (Consider placement in intervention materials or English Language Development Program.)

Diagnostic Assessment Schedule/Pacing

Assessment	Kindergarten	Grade 1	Grade 2	Grade 3
Distinguishing Initial, Medial, and Final Sounds **Phoneme Segmentation Fluency** **Phoneme Deletion** **Phoneme Substitution**	Middle and End of Year	Beginning/Middle of Year	Only if needed	Only if needed
Letter Naming Fluency	Beginning, Middle, End of Year	Beginning of Year	N/A	N/A
Sight Word Fluency	Middle and End of Year	Beginning, Middle, and End of Year	Beginning of Year	N/A
Quick Phonics Survey	Middle and End of Year	Every 4–6 weeks until mastery	Every 4–6 weeks until mastery	Every 4–6 weeks until mastery
Oral Reading Fluency	N/A	Middle and End of Year	Beginning, Middle, and End of Year	Beginning, Middle, and End of Year
Qualitative Spelling Inventory	End of Year	Beginning, Middle, and End of Year	Beginning, Middle, and End of Year	Beginning, Middle, and End of Year
Vocabulary (Critchlow Verbal Language Scale)	Middle and End of Year	Beginning, Middle, and End of Year	Beginning, Middle, and End of Year	Beginning, Middle, and End of Year
Comprehension (Leveled Passages)	N/A	Middle and End of Year	Beginning, Middle, and End of Year	Beginning, Middle, and End of Year
Metacomprehension Strategy Index	N/A	N/A	N/A	Beginning, Middle, and End of Year
Analytic Writing	N/A	Middle and End of Year	Beginning, Middle, and End of Year	Beginning, Middle, and End of Year

K–8 Diagnostic Assessment

Assessment	Grade 4	Grade 5	Grade 6	Grades 7–8
Distinguishing Initial, Medial, and Final Sounds **Phoneme Segmentation Fluency** **Phoneme Deletion** **Phoneme Substitution**	N/A	N/A	N/A	N/A
Letter Naming Fluency	N/A	N/A	N/A	N/A
Sight Word Fluency	N/A	N/A	N/A	N/A
Quick Phonics Survey	Only if needed	Only if needed	Only if needed	Only if needed
Oral Reading Fluency	Beginning, Middle, and End of Year	Beginning, Middle, and End of Year	Beginning, Middle, and End of Year	Beginning, Middle, and End of Year
Qualitative Spelling Inventory	Beginning, Middle, and End of Year	Beginning, Middle, and End of Year	Beginning, Middle, and End of Year	Beginning, Middle, and End of Year
Vocabulary (Critchlow Verbal Language Scale)	Beginning, Middle, and End of Year	Beginning, Middle, and End of Year	Beginning, Middle, and End of Year	Beginning, Middle, and End of Year
Comprehension (Leveled Passages)	Beginning, Middle, and End of Year	Beginning, Middle, and End of Year	Beginning, Middle, and End of Year	Beginning, Middle, and End of Year
Metacomprehension Strategy Index	Beginning, Middle, and End of Year	Beginning, Middle, and End of Year	Beginning, Middle, and End of Year	Beginning, Middle, and End of Year
Analytic Writing	Beginning, Middle, and End of Year	Beginning, Middle, and End of Year	Beginning, Middle, and End of Year	Beginning, Middle, and End of Year

Assessment Record Sheet

Student Name ____________ **Date/Time of Year** ____________

Assessment	Scores	Observations	Next Steps
Phonological Awareness			
Letter Naming Fluency			
Sight Word Fluency			
Quick Phonics Survey			
Oral Reading Fluency			
Qualitative Spelling Inventory			
Vocabulary (Critchlow Verbal Language Scale)			
Comprehension (Leveled Passages)			
Metacomprehension Strategy Index			
Analytic Writing			

Diagnostic Assessment Options

Your state and/or district may have identified a diagnostic assessment for you to use with your students, such as **Fox in a Box** or **TPRI**. It is recommended that you use your approved diagnostic assessment as it aligns with **TREASURES**.

Fox in a Box (K-2)

Description

The kit includes standardized and systematic literacy activities to **diagnose** students' skills in the areas of Phonemic Awareness, Phonics, Reading and Oral Expression, and Listening and Writing. There are benchmark levels for each developmentally appropriate activity. The fox puppet helps make the assessment child friendly.

How to administer

Individually and whole group; record results in a Literacy Progress Record (LPR), which then travels with the student from year to year. Refer to the flow chart in the Teacher's Guide for guidance on how to administer the activities.

When to administer

Administer in early fall and early spring, or more frequently to use as a **progress monitoring** tool. There are specific performance benchmarks and mastery dates to help you plan.

Teacher Tips

Before beginning, familiarize yourself with the activity and gather the necessary materials. Record results directly in the student's LPR, and be sure to include the date when the skill was mastered. Assess all of the students in the same activity before going on to a new activity.

Diagnostic Assessment Options (continued)

TPRI (Texas Primary Reading Inventory) (K–3)

Description

Use for **screening**, **diagnostic**, and **progress monitoring**. These short probes measure **Graphophonemic Knowledge** and **Phonemic Awareness (K–1)**, and **Word Reading (1–3)**, and identify students *not* at risk of reading failure. These are the **diagnostic**, or *Inventory*, subtests:

- **Book and Print Awareness (K)**
- **Phonemic Awareness (K–1)**
- **Listening Comprehension (K–1)**
- **Graphophonemic Knowledge (K–3)**
- **Reading Accuracy (1–3)**
- **Reading Fluency (1–3)**
- **Reading Comprehension (1–3)**

How to administer: Administer individually; follow Branching Rules.

When to administer

Beginning, middle, and end of the year for the **Screening** *(see chart below)* and **Inventory** assessments.

TPRI Link to Treasures

When to Screen	Kindergarten	Grades 1–3
Beginning of the Year	Start mid-year	Unit 1
Middle of the Year	Unit 4	Unit 3
End of the Year	Unit 9	Unit 5

Teacher Tips

Have all the materials ready. Use a standard pronunciation for all sounds. Use the Intervention Skills Guide for additional activities to target specific skills.

Screening/Placement Assessment Options

Oral Reading Fluency

Description

This screening assessment identifies students who may require diagnostic testing and additional instructional support to meet grade-level expectations. There are oral reading fluency passages with explicit and implicit comprehension questions. Student performance is measured by having students do a timed reading of the selected passage. The number of correct words per minute is the oral fluency rate.

How to administer

The student reads a passage while you record any errors on the fluency record sheet. Be sure to start your stopwatch when the student reads the first word. Afterward, the student answers the comprehension questions orally. Calculate the student's words correct per minute rate and check it against the Oral Reading Fluency Norms chart. If a student's WCPM score falls more than ten points below the benchmarks shown on the chart, the student is not reading fluently.

When to administer

Administer the assessment at the beginning, middle, and end of the year.

Teacher Tips

Have each student read at least two passages to evaluate reading performance. It is essential to consider both the norms-based fluency rate and the student's comprehension to determine if further testing and instructional intervention is necessary.

Screening/Placement Assessment Options (continued)

Leveled Passages

Description

This screening assessment identifies whether students are reading below, on, or above grade level. Students identified as reading below level may require diagnostic testing and additional instructional support to meet grade-level expectations. This assessment consists of grade-level passages and comprehension questions. Students' performance is measured through their answers to the comprehension questions.

How to administer

The student silently reads the passages and answers the accompanying questions. Students begin reading passages two grade levels below their current grade (where applicable) and end with the reading of passages two grade levels above their current grade.

When to administer

Administer the assessment at the beginning, middle, and end of the year.

Teacher Tips

You may wish to have students read aloud the passages at their grade level, or the highest level in which they receive above 80% correct on the comprehension questions to assess overall reading fluency.

Other Assessment Opportunities

After the diagnostic, screening, and placement assessments are administered, assessment does not end. Assessment is ongoing and continuous. In fact, good teaching requires that you teach and assess simultaneously, thereby providing immediate corrective feedback and lesson modifications. The following pages detail how informal assessments can be used to confirm (or not) diagnostic assessment results and can lead you to administer additional diagnostic assessments based on observed student needs.

Informal Assessments

The reading classroom is full of assessment opportunities. Chances are you use some of them without realizing you are doing "assessment." Remember the definition of assessment is systematically gathering information about what students know and can do. In reading, you can do this in an informal way throughout instruction.

- **Teach students to monitor their own comprehension.** Monitoring comprehension is an important comprehension strategy explicitly taught in **TREASURES** from Grades one through six. Students can ask themselves questions about what they have just read. Good readers learn to use these metacognitive skills unconsciously. Have you ever said to yourself, "I am not sure what I just read"? Your automatic monitoring system helps you improve your comprehension of the text.
- **Ask students to retell** or explain in their own words what they have just read. A good explanation shows you what a student understands, and a poor explanation makes the student's misconceptions and misunderstandings apparent so you can address them.
- **Teach students how to monitor their own progress.** If children realize they do not understand something they have read, they can try various reading strategies and/or ask for help from peers or from their teacher. Listen for the substance of the answer, and not merely if it is "correct" or not. Learn from the student's answer what he or she is thinking.

Types of Informal Assessments

Quick Checks: TREASURES provides many opportunities for you to observe students independently practice a strategy or skill taught in whole group instruction.

- The Quick Check reminds you to observe your students and see if any of them are having difficulty with a skill they have just learned.
- You can use this information to decide if this is a skill you need to address in small group instruction.

Assignments: Every assignment or activity allows you to assess reading behaviors. Assignments do not need to be formally graded, but they should be treated as a potential source of information about what students know, what they still need to learn, and what their misconceptions or difficulties are.

- Review assignments, noting both strengths and weaknesses, and present the student with oral or written feedback.
- Ask students to go over their own assignments in groups, where peers can point out their strengths and weaknesses to each other. Note that this is an opportunity to show students that looking at what is right and wrong is important.
- Ask students to go over their own work and reflect upon it. This, too, is a skill that needs to be modeled and taught.

Classroom Observations: You have opportunities to observe your students at work and at play, working alone, and interacting with other students. Be systematic with the way you do and record the observations.

- Does this student like to read or look at books? What topics is he or she interested in?
- How does this student work with others?
- You can ask students what kinds of stories or books they like. You should strive to create a print-rich environment, with materials at a wide range of reading levels on as many topics as possible. Expand on students' interests and introduce new ones.

QUICK CHECKS OBSERVATIONS FORM (PRIMARY)

Student's Name	Phonemic Awareness	Phonics	Fluency	Comprehension	Vocabulary

QUICK CHECKS OBSERVATIONS FORM (INTERMEDIATE)

Student's Name	Phonics/Word Study	Fluency	Comprehension	Vocabulary

Assessment Opportunities

Feedback IS Assessment

Using corrective feedback as an assessment tool: Feedback should help students see how they can improve their work. The most useful feedback is a specific comment describing the strengths and weaknesses of individual work, with useful suggestions for improvement. To be useful and motivating, feedback needs to be . . .

- Delivered in the form of praise
- Modeled for the student
- Practiced by the student
- Used continually over time

Feedback can be oral or written: Feedback needs to be immediate. Correct students' errors as soon as they occur.

- Give feedback orally for younger students and nonreaders.
- For older students and good readers, writing positive feedback on their work is helpful. Written comments are more lasting; students can refer back to them.

Asking for feedback: Encourage students to ask for feedback or help when they need it. It is important for students to learn to monitor their own work.

- You can have students place green (I'm OK) and red (I need help) circles or traffic lights on their desk to let you know they need help without disrupting others. Or you can use smiley-faces and frowning-faces for this same purpose.
- This allows you to give feedback and assistance in a timely fashion so that students do not lose momentum or miss something because they were stuck.
- If you use a system like this, the oral feedback you give in response to these requests should follow the same feedback principles. Don't just give "answers." Give feedback that will help the student learn from the mistakes.

How to give good feedback: The table on the next page models some ways for you to provide corrective feedback to your students.

How To Give Corrective Feedback

FEEDBACK SHOULD BE . . .	HOW TO MODEL IT	EXAMPLES
Delivered in the form of praise	Direct your comment at some aspect of the work, not the student. Use descriptive adjectives. Avoid judgmental words. Make I-statements not You-statements.	*DON'T SAY:* "You need to write more about the main character." *SAY:* "The main character was interesting. I want to know more about him." *DON'T SAY:* "Good job!" *SAY:* "Your story makes me want to meet your pet!"
Modeled for the student	Refer to specific aspects of the work. Be specific, not general.	*DON'T SAY:* "The story summary was poor." *SAY:* "The story held my interest. It would be a better story if there were more details."
Practiced by the student	Allow the student to have a turn giving him- or herself feedback.	*DON'T SAY:* "This isn't clear." *SAY:* "You try it now. What suggestion can you make to improve this essay?"
Used continually over time	Provide opportunities for the student to practice giving him- or herself feedback.	*DON'T SAY:* "Tell me what is wrong with your story." *HAVE THE STUDENT RESPOND:* "My story needs a stronger ending."

How to Make Instructional Decisions

What to Do to Make Decisions

To make sound instructional decisions, you should do the following:

- **Interpret:** "This means that he is comprehending beyond grade level because he is good at using context clues. He figures out what the words mean so fast that he skips over some vocabulary and doesn't learn it."
- **Decide** what you can do to meet the student's learning needs.
- **Check:** As you collect ongoing information about student progress, continue to check this information against your interpretation or hypothesis.
- **Modify** your instructional decisions if they are not achieving the intended results.

Compare results from different assessments:

- Look for corroborating evidence across the different kinds of assessments; use multiple measures.
- Different sources of information should reinforce your decisions.

The types of instructional decisions you need to make include the following:

- Decisions about grouping (who to teach).
- Decisions about learning goals and objectives (what to teach).
- Decisions about materials, methods, and rate of instruction (how to teach).

HOW TO MAKE INSTRUCTIONAL DECISIONS

GROUPING

- Will I use small groups? How many do I need?
- How will I decide which student is in which group?
- How will I handle independent work?
- How will I handle whole-class instruction?
- How will I set up the workstations?

LEARNING GOALS OR OBJECTIVES

- Which goals or objectives will I emphasize? Preteach? Reteach?
- Which goals or objectives will require less emphasis?
- In what order will I teach them?

MATERIALS

- Which grade-level materials should be used in reading instruction?
- Which grade-level materials should be available for independent (recreational) reading?
- What topics or kinds of stories would most interest the students?

METHODS

- Which techniques or approaches should I use in lessons?
- Which techniques are best suited for the learning objectives I need to emphasize?
- Which techniques involve students in the learning the most?

RATE OF INSTRUCTION

- How much time should be allotted to each lesson?
- How fast or slow should students be asked to move through particular material?
- What might need to be reviewed several times (take up several lessons) and what might be touched on more lightly?

Making Instructional Decisions

How to Apply Your Decisions

Adjusting Lesson Plans

- Students are achieving the learning targets you set for them, so continue with the next step in the materials, according to your district curriculum.
- Areas of strength are identified, so plan enrichment lessons or activities.
- Areas of difficulty are identified, so plan reteaching lessons.

Identifying Learning Targets

Learning targets for review or remediation should come directly from the assessment information. Share this information with the students so that they understand what their goals and objectives are.

REVIEW or RETEACH?

REVIEW

- For minor difficulties, continue with instruction as planned and incorporate review into seatwork, workstations, or small group instruction.
- Reinforce those concepts during regular instruction, focusing attention on the concept by oral questioning and discussion.
- Example: Students had some difficulty with comma use in the last unit. Proceed to the next unit but incorporate extra practice with commas into daily work and also explicitly point out comma usage in the next stories or text students read.

RETEACH

- Reteach concepts that were difficult for the whole class or for specific groups of students.
- Reteach all or part of a unit by using a mixture of old and new materials. Students can profit from correcting work they have already done and explaining the reasons for the corrections, either orally to you or other students or in writing.
- **Treasures** provides instructional materials at the approaching level for preteaching and reteaching.

Making Instructional Decisions

Modifying Instruction

Changing the Mode of Instruction

- Vary the way you present the skills and concepts.
- Change the kind of student engagement or response required.
- Increase student practice in addition to reteaching the concept.

Choosing Materials

Appropriate materials for reviewing and reteaching are listed in the Teacher's Edition. You can also use skills-based practice readers, trade books, writing resources, practice workbooks, and any other materials that match the learning objectives.

VARY methods for reviewing or reteaching.
Don't repeat what didn't work before!

You can use some of the same materials, but in a different way.

- For example, if a student did not do well on a test or assignment, have him or her go back over it (individually or with a peer tutor or in a small group that does this with each of the members) and say or write *why* the correct answer is correct.
- Do this in a positive manner, giving reasons why an answer is or is not correct.
- If a student can put things in his or her own words, he or she is much more likely to "understand" it.

Use new or different materials and vary the teaching method.

- For example, if using flash cards didn't work the first time for learning a set of vocabulary words, try something else like writing the words in sentences.
- Use more active methods with objectives students find difficult.
- Use several methods for difficult objectives.
- Give more individual feedback in these targeted review areas.
- Allow for student practice, self-assessment, and use of feedback.

Making Instructional Decisions

Modifying Instruction

Look for Patterns in Assessment Results

Sometimes there will be a clear group pattern in the test results.

- Look for a small group of students who missed the same skill or objective.
- Form a group based on this information, and reteach those skills.

Fluency Opportunities

Students whose fluency is below expectations need extra opportunities to practice.

- Additional fluency activities are available in the Fluency Solutions Audio CDs.
- Reading aloud is a motivating way for students to work together. More experienced peers can “coach” their classmates as they listen to them read.
- More experienced peers can get good experience by reading stories aloud to classmates that the less fluent readers would not be able to read themselves.
- Monitor these groups closely, and circulate and assist as needed. Peer tutoring does not work well if the peers act as “substitute teachers.” The teacher needs to remain in the role of supervisor.

Formative Assessment in Fluency Includes Self-Assessment

- Students can use a tape recorder to listen to themselves, and then they can discuss with you what they heard.
- Students may “hear” hesitations or mispronunciations, but they do not know what to do about them. Provide help one-on-one or in small group discussions.

Using the Weekly and Unit Evaluation Sheets

The evaluation sheets that follow each weekly and unit test tell you the specific skills that need to be reviewed or retaught. Compare these results with your own observations.

- Identify one or more objectives from the week or unit that need reinforcement. Add them to your lesson objectives for the next week for one student, for a group of students, or for the whole class, whichever is indicated.
- Decide how you will work these objectives into individual, group, or whole-class work so that the students who need practice get it.

WAYS TO ADDRESS WEAKNESSES

- Reteach skills that a significant number of students are weak in.
- Use appropriate assignments as seatwork and center work during the next unit.
- Form groups for peer tutoring by using one student's strength to assist with another student's weakness. Mix groups often and don't allow one student to always be the "weak" one.
- Use targeted review games as activities.
- Use individual student work as the basis for student conferences. Plan with the student what he or she needs to work on, and how that can be done.

WAYS TO BUILD ON STRENGTHS

- Extend the unit if a significant number of students are strong in the same area. For example, have students read a similar story in one of the leveled texts.
- Add assignments that allow students to excel at something they are good at as seatwork or center work during the next unit.
- Form groups for peer tutoring by using one student's strength to assist with another student's weakness. Mix groups often and don't allow one student to always be the "weak" one.
- Have students make up games or activities that others can play.
- Use individual student work as the basis for student conferences. Help the student explain what exactly the strength is, and plan with the student what he or she will do next as a result.

WAYS TO KEEP INSTRUCTION "ON TRACK"

- Continue with the next unit when possible—incorporating reteaching or extension work as necessary into ongoing progress.
- Keep concepts and skills from previous units of instruction "at the ready" by using games, activities, and seatwork that incorporate systematic review.
- Ask students to identify previous concepts, skills, or reading strategies as they use them (that is, make sure students are aware of what they know).
- Use portfolios or other methods for student self-reflection for reviewing concepts and building a skill repertoire.

K–8 Diagnostic
Assessment

Phonemic Awareness

- Distinguishing Initial, Final, Medial Sounds
- Phoneme Segmentation Fluency
- Phoneme Deletion Test
- Phoneme Substitution Test

Distinguishing Initial, Medial, and Final Sounds

This phonemic awareness test assesses a child's ability to perceive and distinguish sounds in words. Read each word aloud. Ask the child to name the target sound (initial, medial, or final). Record the child's response on the blank. Circle each correct response. Then tally the total number correct. A score of 4 or higher on each subtest indicates proficiency with the skill. A score below 4 indicates that the child may need additional instruction and practice.

Initial Sounds

"Say the first, or beginning, sound in each word."

1. sad ____
2. fish ____
3. top ____
4. ball ____
5. yes ____

Score ____/5

Final Sounds

"Say the last, or final, sound in each word."

1. rat ____
2. bed ____
3. fell ____
4. crib ____
5. pig ____

Score ____/5

Medial Sounds

"Say the middle, or medial, sound in each word."

1. rain ____
2. boat ____
3. cat ____
4. him ____
5. red ____

Score ____/5

Distinguishing Sounds

Initial Sounds

"Listen to the three words. Which word begins with a different sound?"

1. map, man, ham ____
2. leaf, fell, lips ____
3. pen, nest, note ____
4. dog, big, door ____
5. vine, van, fish ____

Score ____/5

Final Sounds

"Listen to the three words. Which word ends with a different sound?"

1. pan, pet, run ____
2. fed, let, hot ____
3. bell, hill, win ____
4. leaf, like, roof ____
5. rob, tip, rope ____

Score ____/5

Medial Sounds

"Listen to the three words. Which word has a different sound in the middle?"

1. feet, need, fight ____
2. coat, hot, road ____
3. sun, nest, rug ____
4. him, his, set ____
5. leg, bag, fed ____

Score ____/5

Phoneme Segmentation Fluency Assessment

Instructions for Administering Phoneme Segmentation

1. Make a copy of the Phoneme Segmentation Fluency record sheet. Use this sheet to record student's oral responses.
2. Say these directions to the student:

   I am going to say a word. Then, you tell me all the sounds you hear in the word. So if I say, "cat" you will say /k/ /a/ /t/. Let's try one. Tell me all the sounds in "hop."
3. If the student gives the correct response, /h/ /o/ /p/, then commend the student.
4. If the student gives an incorrect response, say: *The sounds in "hop" are* /h/ /o/ /p/. Ask the student to repeat the sounds: *Tell me all the sounds in "hop."*
5. Give the student the first word and start your stopwatch. Place a check above each correct sound segment produced. Put a slash (/) through incorrect sounds.
6. The maximum time for each sound segment is 3 seconds. If the student does not provide the next sound segment within 3 seconds, give the student the next word.
7. At the end of 1 minute, stop presenting words and scoring further responses. Add the number of sound segments produced correctly. Record the total number of sound segments produced correctly on the bottom of the scoring sheet.

Directions for Scoring

1. If the student has not given any sound segments correctly in the first 5 words, discontinue the task and put a score of zero. (0)
2. Place a check above the sound segments in the word that are correctly pronounced by the student. The student receives 1 point for each correct part of the word.

   Both of the following examples are correct segmentations of words:

Word	Student Response	Scoring Procedure	Correct Segments
like	"l...i...k"	/l/ /ī/ /k/	3/3
crack	"k..r..a..k"	/k/ /r/ /a/ /k/	4/4

3. Put a slash through segments pronounced incorrectly.
4. See the **Phoneme Segmentation Fluency Growth Table** on page 6 of the Letter Naming and Sight Words section to obtain a phoneme segmentation fluency score.

Name ______________________ Date ______________________

Record Sheet

Phoneme Segmentation Fluency				# correct
man	/m/ /a/ /n/	thing	/th/ /i/ /ng/	___ /6
his	/h/ /i/ /z/	kiss	/k/ /i/ /s/	___ /6
brand	/b/ /r/ /a/ /n/ /d/	match	/m/ /a/ /ch/	___ /8
smile	/s/ /m/ /ī/ /l/	froze	/f/ /r/ /ō/ /z/	___ /8
press	/p/ /r/ /e/ /s/	cheat	/ch/ /ē/ /t/	___ /7
slope	/s/ /l/ /ō/ /p/	tide	/t/ /ī/ /d/	___ /7
blend	/b/ /l/ /e/ /n/ /d/	gate	/g/ /ā/ /t/	___ /8
lost	/l/ /o/ /s/ /t/	shop	/sh/ /o/ /p/	___ /7
jump	/j/ /u/ /m/ /p/	drill	/d/ /r/ /i/ /l/	___ /8
those	/th/ /ō/ /s/	west	/w/ /e/ /s/ /t/	___ /7
plug	/p/ /l/ /u/ /g/	rush	/r/ /u/ /sh/	___ /7
tape	/t/ /ā/ /p/	inch	/i/ /n/ /ch/	___ /6

CORE Phoneme Deletion Test

▶ **WHAT** This assessment includes four phoneme deletion tasks arranged in order of difficulty. The first task assesses the student's ability to delete initial phonemes. For example, the examiner may say the word *cat* and ask the student to say *cat* without the initial /k/ sound. The remaining tasks assess the student's ability to delete final phonemes, such as /t/ in the word *seat*; initial phonemes in blends, such as /s/ in the word *slip*; and phonemes embedded in blends, such as /l/ in the word *play*. The assessment contains minimal grade-level expectations for Grades 1 to 3, but can also be used with older students.

▶ **WHY** These tasks may help to determine whether deficits in phonemic, or sound, awareness account for the student's reading or spelling delays. According to research, the lack of phonemic awareness is the most powerful determinant of the likelihood of a student's failure to learn to read.

▶ **HOW** Before administering each task, administer the Practice Items. For all students, begin with the tasks in Part A of the test. Assess as far as the student can go, regardless of his or her grade placement. Do not correct errors; instead encourage students by praising their willingness to participate. Remember that this is an auditory assessment—students do not see the items on the test. The Correct Response column tells how the student's answer should sound, not how it should be spelled.

PART A

Initial Sound

(Late K and Grade 1)

Begin by saying to the student, "We are going to play a word game. This game will give me information to help teach you better." Then administer the following two Practice Items.

Practice Item 1

TEACHER: Say *cat.*

STUDENT: *cat*

TEACHER: Now say it without the /k/.

STUDENT: *at*

If the student responds incorrectly say, "Let's try that again." For example, if the student says *kit*, model the correct response by emphasizing the /k/ and artificially separating it from the *at.* Help the student to give the correct response by saying each sound slowly. Repeat the Practice Item until the student gives the correct response—even if the student does not seem to understand the task. After the student repeats the correct response, proceed to Practice Item 2.

Practice Item 2

TEACHER: Say *table.*

STUDENT: *table*

TEACHER: Now say it without the /t/.

STUDENT: *able*

If the student responds incorrectly say, "Let's try that again." For example, if the student says *bull*, model the correct response by emphasizing the /t/ and artificially separating it from *able.* Encourage the student to repeat the correct response.

If the student can correctly respond to these two Practice Items, proceed to the Test Items. If the student cannot correctly respond to these Practice Items, skip Part A and proceed to the Practice Items for Part B. Some students may be able to delete a final sound, but not an initial sound.

PART B

Final Sound (Grade 1)

Say to the student, "We are going to play another word game. The rules of this game are a little different. Pay close attention." Then administer the following Practice Item.

Practice Item

TEACHER: Say *seat.*

STUDENT: *seat*

TEACHER: Now say it without the /t/.

STUDENT: *sea*

If the student responds incorrectly say, "Let's try that again." For example, if the student says *keat*, model the correct response by elongating *sea* and artificially separating it from the /t/. Then say, "*Seat* without the /t/ is *sea*." Encourage the student to repeat the correct response.

If the student can correctly respond to the Practice Item, proceed to the Test Items. If the student cannot correctly respond to any of the Part A or B Practice Items, discontinue the assessment.

PART C

First Sound of a Consonant Blend (Grade 2)

Say to the student, "We are going to do something different now. Pay close attention." Then administer the following Practice Item.

Practice Item

TEACHER: Say *slip.*

STUDENT: *slip*

TEACHER: Now say it without the /s/.

STUDENT: *lip*

If the student responds incorrectly say, "Let's try that again." For example, if the student deletes the entire /sl/ blend and says *ip*, model a correct response by emphasizing the /s/ and separating it from *lip*. Say, "Be careful, you're taking off too much. Try to say it without the /s/." If necessary, help the student to repeat the correct response.

If the student can correctly respond to, or repeat, the Practice Item, proceed to the Test Items. If the student can respond correctly to at least two of the Test Items, proceed to Part D; otherwise, discontinue the assessment.

PART D

Embedded Sound of a Consonant Blend (Grade 3)

Say to the student, "We are going to play another word game. The rules of this game are a little different." Then administer the following Practice Item.

Practice Item

TEACHER: Say *play.*

STUDENT: *play*

TEACHER: Now say it without the /l/.

STUDENT: *pay*

If the student responds incorrectly say, "Let's try that again." For example, if the student deletes the entire blend and says *ay*, say: "You are taking off too much. I just wanted you to say it without /l/." Model a correct response by separating all three sounds of the word: /p/ /l/ /ay/, and say: "Without the /l/ it is just /p/ /ay/—*pay.* So, what is *play* without the /l/? Yes, it is *pay*." If necessary, help the student to repeat the correct response.

If the student can correctly respond to, or repeat, the Practice Item, proceed to the Test Items.

▶ **WHAT IT MEANS** Use the guidelines below to determine the student's performance level.

Minimal Grade-Level Expectations

1–6 correct	late K / early Grade 1
7–10 correct	end of Grade 1
11–13 correct	early Grade 2
14–15 correct	end of Grade 2
16–18 correct	early Grade 3
19–20 correct	end of Grade 3

▶ **WHAT'S NEXT** Students who are able to do Part A: Initial Sound are especially ready for formal reading instruction. Students who do not meet grade expectations will benefit from more intense phonemic awareness instruction.

CORE Phoneme Deletion Test

Name ______________________ Grade __________ Date __________

Directions: Follow the format used in the Practice Items to administer the items for each level. Mark "+" to indicate a correct response or "–" to indicate an incorrect response. Write down incorrect responses, but do not correct the student. If the student cannot complete any of the items in Parts A or B, discontinue testing. If the student cannot do at least two items in Part C, discontinue testing. Remember that this is an auditory assessment. Students do not see the items.

Part A: Initial Sound

Practice Items

Say *cat* ... now say it without the /k/ ___(at)

Say *table* ... now say it without the /t/ ___(able)

TEST ITEM	CORRECT RESPONSE		
1. (t)ower	our	(+) (-)	________
2. (c)old	old	(+) (-)	________
3. (b)ake	ache	(+) (-)	________
4. (s)ize	eyes	(+) (-)	________
5. (l)ow	owe	(+) (-)	________

Part B: Final Sound

Practice Items

Say *seat* ... now say it without the /t/ ___(sea)

Say *rake* ... now say it without the /k/ ___(ray)

TEST ITEM	CORRECT RESPONSE		
6. to(n)e	toe	(+)(-)	________
7. droo(p)	drew	(+)(-)	________
8. ti(m)e	tie	(+)(-)	________
9. ro(d)e	row	(+)(-)	________
10. pla(c)e	play	(+)(-)	________

Part C: First Sound of a Consonant Blend

Practice Items

Say *slip* ... now say it without the /s/ ___(lip)

Say *cloud* ... now say it without the /k/ ___(loud)

TEST ITEM	CORRECT RESPONSE		
11. (f)reight	rate	(+) (-)	________
12. (p)layed	laid	(+) (-)	________
13. (s)weet	wheat	(+) (-)	________
14. (b)reak	rake	(+) (-)	________
15. (s)pill	pill	(+) (-)	________

Part D: Embedded Sound of a Consonant Blend

Practice Items

Say *slip* ... now say it without the /l/ ___(sip)

Say *play* ... now say it without the /l/ ___(pay)

TEST ITEM	CORRECT RESPONSE		
16. b(l)end	bend	(+)(-)	________
17. t(w)in	tin	(+)(-)	________
18. g(r)ow	go	(+)(-)	________
19. be(s)t	bet	(+)(-)	________
20. li(f)t	lit	(+)(-)	________

Items Correct ______ **Grade Level** ______

Sound Substitution

This phonemic awareness test assesses a child's ability to manipulate sounds in words. Read each word aloud. Ask the child to replace the target sound with the sound provided. Allow the child to use letter cards to form each word. Record the child's response on the blank. Circle each correct response. Then tally the total number correct. A score of 4 or higher on each subtest indicates proficiency with the skill.

Initial Sound Substitution

"Listen to the word I say. Then replace the first sound with the sound I say."

1. sad Replace the first sound with /m/. ____ (mad)
2. fish Replace the first sound with /d/. ____ (dish)
3. top Replace the first sound with /h/. ____ (hop)
4. ball Replace the first sound with /t/. ____ (tall)
5. light Replace the first sound with /f/. ____ (fight)

Score ____/5

Final Sound Substitution

"Listen to the word I say. Then replace the last sound with the sound I say."

1. bat Replace the last sound with /d/. ____ (bad)
2. pig Replace the last sound with /n/. ____ (pin)
3. tame Replace the last sound with /k/. ____ (take)
4. rib Replace the last sound with /p/. ____ (rip)
5. fish Replace the last sound with /t/. ____ (fit)

Score ____/5

Medial Sound Substitution

"Listen to the word I say. Then replace the middle sound with the sound I say."

1. road Replace the middle sound with /ē/. ____ (read)
2. mean Replace the middle sound with /ā/. ____ (main)
3. top Replace the middle sound with /a/. ____ (tap)
4. ball Replace the middle sound with /e/. ____ (bell)
5. sick Replace the middle sound with /o/. ____ (sock)

Score ____/5

K–8 Diagnostic Assessment

Letter Naming and Sight Words

Letter Naming Fluency Assessment

Instructions for Administering Letter Naming Fluency

1. Place the Letter Naming Fluency record sheet in front of the student.

2. Say these specific directions to the student:

Here are some letters. Tell me the names of as many letters as you can. When I say, "Begin" start here (point to the first letter) *and go across the page. Point to each letter and tell me the name of that letter. If you come to a letter that you don't know, I'll tell it to you. Put your finger on the first letter. Ready, begin.*

3. Start your stopwatch. Follow along with the Letter Naming Fluency record sheet. Put a (/) through letters named incorrectly. Place a check above letters named correctly.

4. At the end of 1 minute, place a bracket (]) after the last letter named and say, *Stop.*

Directions for Scoring

1. If the student does not get any correct letter names within the first 10 letters (1 row), discontinue the task and record a score of zero.

2. If the student hesitates for 3 seconds on a letter, score the letter incorrect, and provide the correct letter to the student.

3. If the student provides the letter sound rather than the letter name, say: *Remember to tell me the letter name, not the sound it makes.* If the student continues providing letter sounds, mark each letter as incorrect, and make a note of this behavior at the bottom of the page.

4. Score a point for each correct letter the student names and record the total number of correct letters at the bottom of the sheet.

5. See the **Letter Naming Fluency Growth Table** on page 6 to obtain a letter naming fluency score.

Name ______________________________ Date ________________

Letter Naming Fluency										# correct
g	a	t	X	r	F	C	j	T	z	__/10
K	l	q	z	b	n	y	s	I	O	__/10
A	e	V	u	Q	Y	z	M	j	a	__/10
f	i	W	R	g	U	d	z	S	c	__/10
k	M	g	D	o	J	n	p	m	h	__/10
C	N	E	b	u	a	g	w	V	f	__/10
G	Y	i	d	e	n	S	T	t	c	__/10
R	F	a	m	Z	I	w	v	C	n	__/10
f	s	P	o	T	W	E	j	k	Q	__/10
D	U	g	e	A	b	i	y	B	d	__/10
N	f	p	R	F	q	l	K	p	M	__/10
L	a	W	f	U	c	O	b	x	Z	__/10

Total ___ /120

Sight Word Fluency Assessment

Instructions for Administering the Assessment

Give the student the assessment sheet, and have the child put his or her finger on the first word in the first row. Explain that you would like the child to read as many words as he or she can in one minute. Tell the child to point to each word and say the word. Then say: *When you are ready, you may begin.* Start your stopwatch, timing the student for one minute as he or she reads the words.

1. Follow along as the child reads. Place a check above each word that is said correctly.
2. Place a line through each word that is read incorrectly or omitted.
3. If the child substitutes or mispronounces a word, put a line through the word and write the word the child said above it.
4. If the child does not correctly say a word within 3 seconds, say the word for the child and mark the word as incorrect.
5. Say *Stop* at the end of one minute and place a bracket (]) after the last word read by the child.

Directions for Scoring

1. Count the total number of words read. This includes the words that are read correctly and incorrectly. Record that number on the table at the bottom of the sheet.
2. Count the number of errors for each line of words in the # of errors column. Record the total number of errors in the bottom table.
3. Use this formula to score Oral Reading Accuracy:

$$\frac{\text{Total No. of Words Read — No. of Errors}}{\text{Total Number of Words Read}} \times 100$$

Name ______________________________ Date ____________________

Sight Word Fluency					# of errors
and	are	do	for	go	(5)
has	have	he	here	is	(5)
like	little	look	me	my	(5)
play	said	see	she	to	(5)
the	this	was	we	what	(5)
where	with	you	jump	not	(5)
up	too	yes	over	run	(5)
come	good	on	that	very	(5)
help	use	now	could	one	(5)
two	they	her	does	who	(5)
some	of	at	live	into	(5)
many	out	want	under	show	(5)

Total number of words read in one minute	
Number of errors	
Accuracy rate (use Oral Reading Accuracy formula)	

K–8 Diagnostic Assessment

AIMSweb® Growth Table
Letter Naming Fluency
Multi-year Aggregate

		Fall		Winter		Spring		
Grade	%ile	Num	LNC	Num	LNC	Num	LNC	ROI
K	90	13377	37	12037	55	12653	65	0.8
	75		25		45		54	0.8
	50		11		33		42	0.9
	25		3		20		31	0.8
	10		0		8		19	0.5
	Mean		15		33		42	0.8
	StdDev		15		17		18	
1	90	10887	65	2518	76	1455	79	0.4
	75		55		66		69	0.4
	50		44		55		58	0.4
	25		32		44		47	0.4
	10		22		32		36	0.4
	Mean		44		55		58	0.4
	StdDev		17		17		17	

Num = Number of Students **LNC** = Letter Names Correct **ROI** = Rate Of Improvement
ROI is Spring Score minus Fall Score (or Winter minus Fall) divided by 36 weeks (or 18 weeks)

AIMSweb® Growth Table
Phoneme Segmentation Fluency
Multi-year Aggregate

		Fall		Winter		Spring		
Grade	%ile	Num	PC	Num	PC	Num	PC	ROI
K	90	1870	44	13234	48	14103	62	0.5
	75		32		34		51	0.5
	50		14		14		37	0.6
	25		3		5		15	0.3
	10		0		0		5	0.1
	Mean		19		20		35	0.4
	StdDev		17		19		22	
1	90	13615	56	10197	62	8269	67	0.3
	75		46		54		59	0.4
	50		33		43		50	0.5
	25		15		31		39	0.7
	10		6		16		26	0.6
	Mean		31		42		48	0.5
	StdDev		19		18		16	

Num = Number of Students **PC** = Phonemes Correct **ROI** = Rate Of Improvement
ROI is Spring Score minus Fall Score (or Winter minus Fall) divided by 36 weeks (or 18 weeks)

K–8 Diagnostic Assessment

Phonics & Decoding

- **Hasbrouck's Quick Phonics Screener**

QPS

Quick Phonics Screener, Standard Version

Jan Hasbrouck, Ph.D.

The purpose of the Quick Phonics Screener (QPS) is to provide informal diagnostic information that can be used to help (a) PLAN a student's instructional program in basic word reading skills, and (b) MONITOR THE PROGRESS or IMPROVEMENT in phonics skill development. The QPS has not been normed or standardized. It is meant to be used as an informal classroom assessment tool.

Directions for Administration and Scoring

1. Say to the student:

   "I'm going to ask you to read some letters, words, and sentences to me so I can find out what kinds of words are easy for you to read and what kinds of words you still need to learn. I want you to try to do your best. We probably won't do this whole page; we'll stop if it gets too hard. Do you have any questions?"

   Start the QPS assessment where you believe the student's skills are fairly strong. For beginning readers (K–1 level), start with sounds or letter names.

   For the *NAMES* task, have the student name the letter Q, not the *qu* digraph. For the *SOUNDS* task, have the student give you the short sound for each of the vowels. If the student says the long sound (letter name), say: *"That is one sound that letter makes. Do you know the short sound for that letter?"* For the letter *c*, ask for the "hard sound" /k/, as in *cat*. For the letter *g* ask for the "hard sound" /g/, as in *gas*. For the letter *y* ask for the /y/ sound, as in *yes*. If the student offers a correct alternative sound for these letters, you should say, *"Yes, that is one sound for that letter. Do you know another sound that letter makes?"*

   Most students in 4th grade and above would not be given the letter names/sounds task. Letter names would usually only be given to K–1st students. (If a student reads 6/10 or more in Task 2a, you may skip Task 1 Letter Sounds.)

2. If the student has difficulty (half or fewer correct on any task) move up the page to an easier task. If the student does well (more than half correct on a task), move down to a harder task.

3. On Tasks 2–6: If the student reads all or almost all words correctly on part (a) of the task (reading words), you may want to skip part (b) of the task (reading sentences). If the next task is difficult for the student, you can go back and complete the part of a previous task that was skipped.

4. When the student is reading the words in text, only count errors on the target words (those underlined and in italics).

5. Stop the assessment when the student appears frustrated or tired. It is OK to stop in the middle of a task. Not all tasks must be administered, but try to assess as many as possible so you will have sufficient information to plan instruction or monitor progress.

6. Mark errors and make notes or comments to help you remember how the student responded. Note that in Task 9, students read the entire word, not syllable- by -syllable. The teacher's copy is written in syllables to facilitate marking/recording of errors within a word.

7. The QPS is scored by each individual task *only.* Record the ratio of correct responses over the total number possible, (e.g., 13/21 or 8/10 for each task). A chart format can be helpful for reporting QPS results.

1. Letters		Score
(a) Names	N/A not administered	____ /26
(b) Sounds		18 /21 cons. 4 /5 vowels
2. VC and CVC		**Score**
(a) List		8 /10
(b) Text		17 /20
3. Digraphs		**Score**
(a) List		6 /10
(b) Text		4 /10

8. The grade level listed above each task is an approximate level at which those phonics skills are often taught. **NOTE**: *Results from the QPS **CAN ONLY** be used to determine a student's strengths/needs in key phonics and decoding skills, **NOT** his or her grade-level performance in reading.*

Quick Phonics Screener—Standard Version

Task									
Task 1(a)	m	t	a	s	i	r	d	f	o
	g	l	h	u	c	n	b	j	k
Task 1(b)	y	e	w	p	v	qu	x	z	

Task					
Task 2(a)	wat	fod	leb	tum	pon
	sib	cug	raf	mip	hev
Task 2(b)	Sam and Ben hid the gum. Pat had a nap in bed. Mom had a top on a big pot. Tim can sit in a tub.				

Task					
Task 3(a)	shap	ming	gack	whum	pith
	chan	thog	kosh	mich	whaf
Task 3(b)	That duck had a wet wing. When can Chip pack?		Brad hit a log with a whip. A fish is in that tub.		

Task					
Task 4(a)	clab	trin	snaf	greb	slad
	fosp	lonk	mant	jast	sund
Task 4(b)	Glen will swim past the raft in the pond. The frog must flip and spin and jump.				

Task					
Task 5(a)	sice	nole	fune	moze	vate
	rine	lade	sile	gane	fote
Task 5(b)	Mike and Jane use a rope to ride the mule. Pete had five tapes at home.				

Quick Phonics Screener—Standard Version

Task					
Task 6(a)	cort tarn	pirk forp	varb murk	serl tirn	surd kerm
Task 6(b)	The tar on his torn shirt burned and hurt him. The bird hid under the short ferns in the park.				

Task					
Task 7(a)	litch gerb	mudge knaz	glux gnap	quam wrill	celp ralk
Task 7(b)	The cider is in the wrong cup. She ran to the center of the bridge. I will stitch a knot on the quilt. The giant can gnaw on the box.				

Task								
Task 8	foat	roast	frea	creak	moom	scoop	raim	waist
	folt	scold	dray	gray	chout	mount	poid	join
	moy	royal	vaul	fault	praw	straw	koe	toe
	frew	jewel	palk	scald	pigh	fight		

Task					
Task 9(a)	mascot puzzle	basket cartoon	moment order	bacon escape	handle chowder
Task 9(b)	amputate practical	liberty innocent	dominate electric	elastic volcano	entertain segregate
Task 9(c)	particular evaporate	contaminate inventory	community prehistoric	superior solitary	vitality emergency

Task						
Task 10	discount	dismiss	nonsense	nostop	index	intent
	prefix	prepare	return	regard	unable	uncertain
	confident	concert	station	motion	famous	joyous
	madness	witness	portable	drinkable	fastest	dampest
	mouthful	fearful	honorary	literary	instrument	fragment

K–8 Diagnostic Assessment

Grades K–1															
1. Letters							Score								Score
(a) Names	m	t	a	s	i	r		**(b) Sounds**	/m/	/t/	/**a**/	/s/	/**i**/	/r/	
	d	f	o	g	l	h			/d/	/f/	/**o**/	/g/	/l/	/h/	/21 cons.
	u	c	n	b	j	k			/**u**/	/k/	/n/	/b/	/j/	/k/	
	y	e	w	p	v	qu			/y/	/**e**/	/w/	/p/	/v/	/kw/	
	x	z					/26		/ks/	/z/					/5 vowels

Grade 1						
2. VC and CVC					Comments	Score
(a) In List	wat	fod	leb	tum		
	pon	sib	cug	raf		
	mip	hev				/10
(b) In Text	*Sam* and *Ben* *hid* the *gum*.		*Pat* *had* a *nap* *in* *bed*.			
	Mom *had* a *top* *on* a *big* *pot*.		*Tim* *can* *sit* *in* a *tub*.			/20

Grade 1						
3. Consonant Digraphs					Comments	Score
(a) In List	shap	ming	gack	whum		
	pith	chan	thog	kosh		
	mich	whaf				/10
(b) In Text	*That* *duck* had a wet *wing*.		*Brad* hit a log *with* a *whip*.			
	When can *Chip* *pack*?		A *fish* is in *that* tub.			/10

Grade 1						
4. CVCC and CCVC					Comments	Score
(a) In List	clab	trin	snaf	greb		
	slad	fosp	lonk	mant		
	jast	sund				/10
(b) In Text	*Glen* will *swim* *past* the *raft* in the *pond*.					
	The *frog* *must* *flip* and *spin* and *jump*.					/10

Grades 1–2						
5. Silent e					Comments	Score
(a) In List	sice	nole	fune	moze		
	vate	rine	lade	sile		
	gane	fote				/10
(b) In Text	*Mike* and *Jane* *use* a *rope* to *ride* the *mule*.					
	Pete had *five* *tapes* at *home*.					/10

K–8 Diagnostic Assessment

Grades 1–2			
6. r-Controlled Vowels		Comments	Score
(a) In List	cort pirk varb serl surd tarn forp murk tirn kerm		/10
(b) In Text	The _tar_ on his _torn_ _shirt_ _burned_ and _hurt_ him. The _bird_ hid _under_ the _short_ _ferns_ in the _park_.		/10

Grades 1–3			
7. Advanced Consonants (–tch, -dge, -x, qu, soft c & g, kn, gn, wr, -lk)		Comments	Score
(a) In List	litch mudge glux quam celp gerb knaz gnap wrill ralk		/10
(b) In Text	The _cider_ is in the _wrong_ cup. She ran to the _center_ of the _bridge_. I will _stitch_ a _knot_ on the _quilt_. The _giant_ can _gnaw_ on the _box_.		/10

Grades 1–3			
8. Vowel Teams		Comments	Score
oa, ea, oo, ai, ol, ay, ou, oi, oy, au, aw, oe, ew, al, igh	foat roast frea creak moom scoop raim waist folt scold dray gray chout mount poid join moy royal vaul fault praw straw koe toe frew jewel palk scald pigh fight		/30

Grades 2, 3, 4–6+			
9. Multi-Syllable		Comments	Score
(a) 2-Syllable	mas-cot bas-ket mo-ment ba-con han-dle puz -zle car-toon or-der es-cape chow-der		/10
(b) 3-Syllable	am-pu-tate lib-er-ty dom-in-ate e-las-tic en-ter-tain prac-ti-cal in-no-cent e-lec-tric vol-ca-no seg-re-gate		/10
(c) 4-Syllable	par-tic-u-lar con-tam-in-ate com-mu-ni-ty su-per-i-or vi-tal-i-ty e-vap-or-ate in-ven-tor-y pre-his-tor-ic sol-i-tar-y e-mer-gen-cy		/10

Grades 2, 3, 4–6+			
10. Prefixes and Suffixes		Comments	Score
dis-, non-, in-, pre-, re-, un-, con-, -tion, -ous, -ness, -able, -est, -ful, -ary, -ment	discount dismiss nonsense nonstop index intent prefix prepare return regard unable uncertain confident concert station motion famous joyous madness witness portable drinkable fastest dampest mouthful fearful honorary literary instrument fragment		/30

K–8 Diagnostic Assessment

Oral Reading Fluency

- **Fluency Passages for Grades K–8**
- **National Fluency Norms**

Introduction

What Is Fluency?

Fluency is the critical bridge between two key elements of reading—decoding and comprehension. In its 2000 report, the National Reading Panel defined it as "the ability to read text quickly, accurately, and with proper expression." Fluency has several dimensions. Successful readers must decode words accurately. But they must move beyond decoding and recognize words in connected text quickly and automatically. They must also read with expression in order to bring meaningful interpretation to the text. All three dimensions—accurate decoding, automaticity, and ability to read expressively—work together to create effective comprehension and overall success in reading.

In its 1994 study of reading, the National Assessment of Educational Progress (NAEP) established a clear connection between fluency and comprehension. NAEP defined fluency as the ease or "naturalness" of reading. It recognized certain key elements as contributing to fluency. These included the reader's grouping or phrasing of words as shown through intonation, stress, and pauses and the reader's adherence to the author's syntax. They also included expressiveness as reflected by the reader's interjection of a sense of feeling, anticipation, or characterization in oral reading. These elements are called *prosody*. When readers use appropriate volume, tone, emphasis, and phrasing, they give evidence of comprehension. They demonstrate that they are actively constructing meaning from the text.

Why Is Fluency Important?

Fluency is critical because it directly impacts the comprehension process. For years, teachers thought that if students could decode words accurately, they would become strong readers. Fluency, which has been referred to as a "neglected" aspect of reading, received little attention. Now it is recognized as one of the five critical components of reading.

Researchers have pointed out that people can successfully focus on only one thing at a time. They can, however, do more than one thing at a time if one of those things is so well learned that it can be done automatically. In its simplest form, reading can be seen as (1) word identification or decoding and (2) comprehension, or the active construction of meaning. Effective readers cannot focus on both of these processes at the same time. If a reader is focused almost entirely on decoding, that reader will have few resources left over for constructing meaning. Only when readers can read the words in connected text automatically are they free to focus their attention on making inferences, drawing conclusions, and applying other critical thinking skills associated with constructing meaning.

A fluent reader generally reads with speed and accuracy, but in addition usually displays these kinds of behaviors:

- Recognizes words automatically
- Applies graphophonic, semantic, and syntactic cues to recognize unfamiliar words

- Segments texts into meaningful chunks
- Emulates the sounds and rhythms of spoken language while reading aloud

A nonfluent reader, in contrast, may display these kinds of behaviors:

- Reads slowly and laboriously
- Processes text word-by-word in a choppy manner
- Frequently ignores punctuation
- Fails to use meaningful phrasing
- Shows little certainty when reading high-frequency words

Fluency does not mean only rapid reading. Occasionally, you will come across a nonfluent reader who is able to read text rapidly but fails to use appropriate phrasing. This reader often ignores meaning and punctuation. As a result, this reader struggles to answer questions about what has been read and fails to grasp the intent of the text.

Why Assess Fluency?

Students need to be fluent in order to be proficient readers. Their oral reading fluency can be improved through explicit training, but you need to assess their fluency level before you can determine what specific fluency-building activities and materials will be appropriate. In addition, students excel in reading when they are given opportunities to read as much connected text as possible at their independent level. Fluency assessment helps you determine what this level is.

The oral reading fluency assessments in this book answer this question: *How many words can a student read aloud per minute and how many of these words are read correctly?* This book also helps you observe reading performance beyond speed and accuracy by providing a rubric similar to the one developed by NAEP. This 4-level rubric on page 4 takes into account additional aspects of fluency, such as prosody.

How and When to Assess

Kindergarten Through Early First Grade

Until children can decode and automatically recognize many words by sight, they cannot be expected to read aloud effortlessly and expressively. That is why formally assessing their oral reading fluency at this early stage is not recommended. However, it is highly recommended that kindergarten children be involved in fluency-building activities, such as listening to books being read aloud and imitating auditory models of natural speech. Toward the end of kindergarten, children can be given opportunities to reread familiar, predictable, and decodable text to build fluency.

Some assessments for children at these grade levels are considered valuable. By assessing letter naming, phoneme segmentation, and sight word fluency during kindergarten and the early part of Grade 1, teachers can determine what type of fluency-building activities and materials to provide. Assessments for these skill areas appear in other sections of this book.

Midyear of Grade 1 Through Grade 8

Curriculum-based assessment of oral reading fluency is administered by asking a student to do a timed reading of a carefully selected on-level passage. As the student reads, you follow along in a copy of the same text and record errors such as omissions, substitutions, misreadings, insertions of words or parts of words, and hesitations of more than three seconds. Self-corrections and repetitions are not considered errors. To calculate the number of words read correctly in one minute, subtract the number of errors from the total number of words read. This process should be repeated periodically throughout the school year to monitor growth.

The Fluency Passages

The fluency passages serve two purposes. They can be administered three times a year as benchmark tests to determine if students are on track. They can also be used every unit so that you can monitor progress and determine if students are meeting instructional goals.

Oral Fluency Scale

Prosody Rubric

Level 4

- The student: reads in large, meaningful phrases; may occasionally repeat words or short phrases, but the overall structure and syntax of the passage is not affected; reads at an appropriate rate of speed with expressive interpretation.

Level 3

- The student: reads in three- and four-word phrases; reads primarily in phrases that preserve the passage's syntax and structure; attempts to read expressively; generally reads at an appropriate rate of speed.

Level 2

- The student: reads mainly in two-word phrases, with some longer phrases and at times word-by-word; may group words awkwardly and not connect phrases to the larger context of the passage; reads sections of the passage excessively slowly or quickly.

Level 1

- The student: reads word-by-word, with some longer phrases; does not phrase meaningfully or with an appropriate rate of speed; reads the passage excessively slowly.

Curriculum-Based Oral Reading Fluency Norms

Use these norms to interpret your students' oral reading fluency abilities and to tailor instruction to their individual needs. Results are based on a one-minute timed sampling of students reading aloud. A more detailed chart appears on pages 102–103.

Grade	Percentile	Fall WCPM	Winter WCPM	Spring WCPM
1	90	NA	81	111
	75	NA	47	82
	50	NA	23	53
	25	NA	12	28
	10	NA	6	15
	SD	NA	32	39
2	90	106	125	142
	75	79	100	117
	50	51	72	89
	25	25	42	61
	10	11	18	31
	SD	37	41	42
3	90	128	146	162
	75	99	120	137
	50	71	92	107
	25	44	62	78
	10	21	36	48
	SD	40	43	44
4	90	145	166	180
	75	119	139	152
	50	94	112	123
	25	68	87	98
	10	45	61	72
	SD	40	41	43
5	90	166	182	194
	75	139	156	168
	50	110	127	139
	25	85	99	109
	10	61	74	83
	SD	45	44	45
6	90	177	195	204
	75	153	167	177
	50	127	140	150
	25	98	111	122
	10	68	82	93
	SD	42	45	44
7	90	180	192	202
	75	156	165	177
	50	128	138	150
	25	102	109	123
	10	79	88	98
	SD	40	43	41
8	90	185	193	199
	75	161	173	177
	50	133	146	151
	25	106	115	124
	10	77	84	97
	SD	43	45	41

A student's scores should fall within a range of ten WCPM above or below the score shown.

KEY
WCPM: Words correct per minute
SD: Average standard deviation of scores

SOURCE Hasbrouck, J. & Tindal, G. (2005) norms for oral reading fluency. Eugene, OR: Behavioral Research & Teaching, University of Oregon.

Administering Fluency Assessments and Using the Fluency Record

Directions

Give a student a reading passage he or she has not seen before. Fluency assessments are always done as "cold reads"; that is, they are done with material that is new to the person being tested. Explain that you would like the student to read the passage out loud and then answer two questions about it. Then say: *When you are ready, you may begin.* Start your stopwatch when the student reads the first word.

1. Follow along on your copy of the passage as the student reads. Place a line through each word that is read incorrectly or omitted.
2. Place a check above each word that is read correctly.
3. If the student substitutes or mispronounces a word, put a line through the word and write the word the student said above it.
4. If the student does not correctly say the word within 3 seconds, say the word for the student and circle the word to mark it as incorrect. Self-corrections and repetitions are not marked as errors.
5. At the end of one minute, stop your stopwatch and place a bracket (]) after the last word read by the student.
6. Have the student finish reading the passage.
7. Read the comprehension questions to the student. Have the student answer the comprehension questions orally.

How to Score

Record the information for each student on the fluency record sheet for that passage.

1. Look at the number in the left margin of the passage, on the same line as the bracket. (Note: In hyphenated words, individual words are counted as one word.) Add to this number all the words before the bracket to figure out how many words the student was able to read in one minute.
2. Count each word you circled or put a line through. The total is the number of errors made. Subtract this number from the number of words read in one minute to arrive at the Oral Reading Fluency Rate, or Words Correct Per Minute score.
3. Use this formula to score Oral Reading Accuracy:

   $$\frac{\text{Total No. of Words Read} - \text{No. of Errors}}{\text{Total Number of Words Read}} \times 100$$

   An Oral Reading Accuracy Scoring Chart is also provided on the inside of the back cover to help you calculate the percentage.

4. On the Prosody Rubric, circle 1, 2, 3, or 4 depending on your evaluation of the student's performance. A score of 4 is the highest possible score.
5. Write comments about oral reading performance on the sheet, including the student's ability to answer the comprehension questions.

Scoring Sample

The Oral Fluency Record Sheet is an assessment tool to help you record oral reading accuracy and important aspects of oral reading fluency. Information gathered from the fluency record sheet may be used to verify or clarify instructional decisions.

Oral Reading Accuracy is a percentage score based on the total number of words read and the number of errors noted. The student should read 97% or more of the words correctly. A scoring chart for measuring Oral Reading Accuracy is provided on the inside back cover for your convenience.

Oral Reading Fluency is a score that is equivalent to the total number of words read in one minute minus the number of errors made.

Oral Fluency Record Sheet

Name____________________ **Date**__________

Oral Reading Accuracy: __________% **Circle: Fall Winter Spring**

Oral Reading Fluency Score: __________ **words correct per minute**

Prosody Rubric: (Circle Score) 1 2 3 4

The Prosody Rubric is a rubric for evaluating oral reading performance. It groups observable behaviors into levels.

Comprehension Question Responses

#1 ____________________

#2 ____________________

Scoring Sample

✓ ✓ ✓ ✓ ✓ ✓ ✓ ✓ ✓ ✓ ✓
Jane and Dean were best pals. They rode their bikes to
✓ ✓ ✓ ✓ ✓ ✓ ✓ ✓ ✓
11 school (together.) At recess, they always played on the same
✓ ✓ ✓ ✓ ✓ ✓ ✓ ✓ ✓ ✓ ✓ ✓
21 team. Jane and Dean like to race home at school and do their
✓ ✓ ✓ ✓ ✓ ✓ ✓ ✓ ✓
34 homework together. Then Pepper came along. Pepper was Jane's
✓ ✓ ✓ ✓ ✓ ✓ ✓ ✓ ✓ ✓ ✓ ✓ ✓
43 new black puppy. Dean felt bad because Jane spent all her time with
✓ ✓ ✓ ✓ ✓ ✓ ✓ ✓ ✓ ✓ ✓ ✓ ✓
57 Pepper now. Dean missed his best friend. One day, Dean sat on his
✓ ✓ ✓ ✓ ✓ ✓ ✓ ✓ ✓ ✓ ✓ ✓
71 (front) steps alone. He closed his eyes and thought about all the fun
✓ ✓ ✓ ✓ ✓ ✓ ✓
85 he and Jane used to have. Suddenly,] something licked his face and

97 Dean opened his eyes. Jane and Pepper had come to play. Now Dean

111 had two best pals. **114**

No. of words read corrrectly: 92/114

No. of errors made: 3/114

The Bug

I see a bug. It has six legs.
It is red. It is very small.
It is fun to look at it.
The bug is very busy.
I see it go up a hill.
I see it come down.
I see it dig. I see it stop.
The sun is out now. It is a hot sun.
It is time for a nap.
The bug naps in the sun.
I will nap in the sun, too.

1. What is this story mostly about?
2. Why does the bug take a nap?

Oral Fluency Record Sheet

Name ______________________ Date ______________

Oral Reading Accuracy: __________% **Circle: Fall Winter Spring**

Oral Reading Fluency Score: __________ **words correct per minute**

Prosody Rubric: (Circle Score) 1 2 3 4

Comprehension Question Responses

#1 ______________________________

#2 ______________________________

The Bug

	I see a bug. It has six legs.
8	It is red. It is very small.
15	It is fun to look at it.
22	The bug is very busy.
27	I see it go up a hill.
34	I see it come down.
39	I see it dig. I see it stop.
47	The sun is out now. It is a hot sun.
57	It is time for a nap.
63	The bug naps in the sun.
69	I will nap in the sun, too. **76**

Number of words read: __________ **Number of errors made:** __________

Ben's Birthday

Today is Ben's birthday.
I am helping Mom make a cake.
We mix eggs and milk.
Then Mom adds more good things.
The batter is thick and white.
Mom puts the batter into a pan.
She puts the pan into the oven.
"I think Ben will like his cake," I say.
Time passes. Then I think I smell smoke.
Is it the cake? Mom runs in. But the cake is fine.
Now we are ready for Ben's birthday.
Dad picks Ben up to see his cake.
Ben smiles and claps his hands.
"You are one year old today!" we all say.

1. What is the story about?
2. Why couldn't Ben bake the cake?

Oral Fluency Record Sheet

Name ______________________________ Date ______________

Oral Reading Accuracy: ________% Circle: Fall Winter Spring

Oral Reading Fluency Score: ____________ words correct per minute

Prosody Rubric: (Circle Score) 1 2 3 4

Comprehension Question Responses

#1 ______________________________

#2 ______________________________

Ben's Birthday

	Today is Ben's birthday.
4	I am helping Mom make a cake.
11	We mix eggs and milk.
16	Then Mom adds more good things.
22	The batter is thick and white.
28	Mom puts the batter into a pan.
35	She puts the pan into the oven.
42	"I think Ben will like his cake," I say.
51	Time passes. Then I think I smell smoke.
59	Is it the cake? Mom runs in. But the cake is fine.
71	Now we are ready for Ben's birthday.
78	Dad picks Ben up to see his cake.
86	Ben smiles and claps his hands.
92	"You are one year old today!" we all say. 101

Number of words read: ________ Number of errors made: ________

You and Your Shadow

Do you like to play with your shadow?
You can use your hands to make pictures on a wall.
You can make animal heads and funny shapes.
Light makes the shadows.
Light might hit you on one side.
Your shadow would fall on the other side.
When you are outside, sunlight makes shadows.
The sun may make long shadows or short ones.
In the morning and evening, the sun is low.
Shadows are long.
At noon, the sun is high. Shadows are short.
Is your shadow in front of you?
Then the light is behind you.
Is your shadow behind you?
Then the light is in front of you.
You are never alone. You always have your shadow.

1. What makes shadows?
2. What would your shadow look like in the morning?

Oral Fluency Record Sheet

Name ______________________________ Date ______________

Oral Reading Accuracy: ________% **Circle: Fall Winter Spring**
Oral Reading Fluency Score: ____________ **words correct per minute**
Prosody Rubric: (Circle Score) 1 2 3 4
Comprehension Question Responses
#1 ______________________________
#2 ______________________________

You and Your Shadow

	Do you like to play with your shadow?
8	You can use your hands to make pictures on a wall.
19	You can make animal heads and funny shapes.
27	Light makes the shadows.
31	Light might hit you on one side.
38	Your shadow would fall on the other side.
46	When you are outside, sunlight makes shadows.
53	The sun may make long shadows or short ones.
62	In the morning and evening, the sun is low.
71	Shadows are long.
74	At noon, the sun is high. Shadows are short.
83	Is your shadow in front of you?
90	Then the light is behind you.
96	Is your shadow behind you?
101	Then the light is in front of you.
109	You are never alone. You always have your shadow. **118**

Number of words read: __________ **Number of errors made:** __________

Our American Flag

Our flag is special to us.
It stands for our country. It is red, white, and blue.
The flag has 13 stripes. It has 50 stars.
There were 13 states when our country was born.
There are 50 states in our country now.
We call our flag the Stars and Stripes.
That is what we see when we look at the flag.
Here are some rules about the flag.
Fly the flag outside in good weather.
Take the flag down at night.
Take the flag inside when it rains.
Never let the flag touch the ground.
Follow these rules.
They show that you are proud of your flag.

1. What does each star stand for on the flag?
2. How can you care for your flag?

Oral Fluency Record Sheet

Name ______________________________ Date ______________

Oral Reading Accuracy: ________% Circle: Fall Winter Spring

Oral Reading Fluency Score: ____________ words correct per minute

Prosody Rubric: (Circle Score) 1 2 3 4

Comprehension Question Responses

#1 ______________________________

#2 ______________________________

Our American Flag

	Our flag is special to us.
6	It stands for our country. It is red, white, and blue.
17	The flag has 13 stripes. It has 50 stars.
26	There were 13 states when our country was born.
35	There are 50 states in our country now.
43	We call our flag the Stars and Stripes.
51	That is what we see when we look at the flag.
62	Here are some rules about the flag.
69	Fly the flag outside in good weather.
76	Take the flag down at night.
82	Take the flag inside when it rains.
89	Never let the flag touch the ground.
96	Follow these rules.
99	They show that you are proud of your flag. **108**

Number of words read: __________ Number of errors made: __________

The New Friend

Jane and Dean were best pals. They rode their bikes to school together every day. They were both in Mrs. Green's class. At recess, they always played on the same baseball team. Jane and Dean liked to race home after school and do their homework together.

Then Pepper came along. Pepper was Jane's new black puppy. Dean felt sad because Jane spent all her time with Pepper now. Dean missed his best friend.

One day, Dean sat on his front steps alone. He closed his eyes and thought about all the fun he and Jane used to have.

Suddenly, something licked his face, and Dean opened his eyes. Jane and Pepper had come to play. Now Dean had two best pals.

1. Why was Dean sad?
2. Why do you think Jane and Pepper came to play?

Oral Fluency Record Sheet

Name ______________________________ Date ______________

Oral Reading Accuracy: ________% **Circle:** Fall Winter Spring
Oral Reading Fluency Score: __________ words correct per minute
Prosody Rubric: (Circle Score) 1 2 3 4
Comprehension Question Responses
#1 ______________________________
#2 ______________________________

The New Friend

	Jane and Dean were best pals. They rode their
9	bikes to school together every day. They were both
18	in Mrs. Green's class. At recess, they always
26	played on the same baseball team. Jane and Dean
35	liked to race home after school and do their
44	homework together.
46	Then Pepper came along. Pepper was Jane's
53	new black puppy. Dean felt sad because Jane
61	spent all her time with Pepper now. Dean missed
70	his best friend.
73	One day, Dean sat on his front steps alone. He
83	closed his eyes and thought about all the fun he
93	and Jane used to have.
98	Suddenly, something licked his face, and Dean
105	opened his eyes. Jane and Pepper had come to
114	play. Now Dean had two best pals. **121**

Number of words read: ________ **Number of errors made:** ________

Sharks

Sharks have lived on Earth for years and years. Today there are more than 350 different kinds. Sharks come in many sizes. The whale shark can be 36 feet in length. The smallest shark grows only to about 6 inches. Some sharks have big, sharp teeth. Others have very small teeth. But all sharks have one thing in common. They all must open their mouths to breathe. Sharks must keep their mouths open when they swim, or they will die.

Every year sharks are killed for many reasons. They get caught in fishing nets. Some are caught to be sold for shark meat or shark fin soup. Shark skin is sometimes used for belts. Other people hunt them because they think sharks are dangerous. Will sharks be around much longer?

1. How does a shark breathe?
2. Why are sharks in danger?

Oral Fluency Record Sheet

Name ______________________________ Date ______________

Oral Reading Accuracy: __________% Circle: Fall Winter Spring

Oral Reading Fluency Score: ______________ words correct per minute

Prosody Rubric: (Circle Score) 1 2 3 4

Comprehension Question Responses

#1 ______________________________

#2 ______________________________

Sharks

	Sharks have lived on Earth for years and years.
9	Today there are more than 350 different kinds. Sharks
18	come in many sizes. The whale shark can be 36
28	feet in length. The smallest shark grows only to about
38	6 inches. Some sharks have big, sharp teeth.
46	Others have very small teeth. But all sharks have one
56	thing in common. They all must open their mouths to
66	breathe. Sharks must keep their mouths open when
74	they swim, or they will die.
80	Every year sharks are killed for many
87	reasons. They get caught in fishing nets. Some
95	are caught to be sold for shark meat or shark fin
106	soup. Shark skin is sometimes used for belts.
114	Other people hunt them because they think
121	sharks are dangerous. Will sharks be around
128	much longer? **130**

Number of words read: __________ Number of errors made: __________

Fun for Marge

Marge the cat did not feel like chasing mice today. She wanted some fun for a change. Marge strolled across the street and into a schoolyard. She wanted to watch what the children were doing there.

Marge slid through the door and hid in a cardboard box. Not long after that, someone picked up the box. Marge swayed as she was carried through a narrow hall. Then the swaying stopped.

In a flash, Marge was out of the box. She could not believe her eyes. All the children were running and chasing balls. Marge thought they were all pretending to be cats, and joined in the game.

Soon the children were chasing Marge, but she did not like this kind of fun. Marge ran down the hall and out the door. After that day, Marge thought chasing mice was just enough fun for a feline.

1. Why did Marge go to the schoolyard?
2. Why would Marge think the children were pretending to be cats?

Oral Fluency Record Sheet

Name ______________________________ Date ______________

Oral Reading Accuracy: ________% **Circle: Fall Winter Spring**

Oral Reading Fluency Score: ____________ **words correct per minute**

Prosody Rubric: (Circle Score) 1 2 3 4

Comprehension Question Responses

#1 ______________________________

#2 ______________________________

Fun for Marge

	Marge the cat did not feel like chasing mice
9	today. She wanted some fun for a change. Marge
18	strolled across the street and into a schoolyard.
26	She wanted to watch what the children were
34	doing there.
36	Marge slid through the door and hid in a
45	cardboard box. Not long after that, someone picked
53	up the box. Marge swayed as she was carried
62	through a narrow hall. Then the swaying stopped.
70	In a flash, Marge was out of the box. She could
81	not believe her eyes. All the children were running and
91	chasing balls. Marge thought they were all pretending
99	to be cats, and joined in the game.
107	Soon the children were chasing Marge,
113	but she did not like this kind of fun. Marge ran
124	down the hall and out the door. After that day,
134	Marge thought chasing mice was just enough
141	fun for a feline. **145**

Number of words read: __________ **Number of errors made:** __________

The White House

The White House is the home of the President of the United States. It is indeed a big, white house. A painter would need 570 gallons of white paint to cover all the outside walls!

The White House has 6 floors, 132 rooms, and 32 bathrooms. Some rooms are for the President's family and friends. Other rooms are used as offices or for meetings. Parties and other celebrations are held in some rooms. The biggest room is the East Room. It is used for balls and parties. The President has small dinners in the Blue Room. Big dinners, on the other hand, take place in the State Dining Room.

You would enjoy a visit to the White House. The tour takes you to five of the rooms. You might even meet the President!

1. What is this story about?
2. Tell what three of the rooms in the White House are used for.

Oral Fluency Record Sheet

Name ______________________________ Date ______________

Oral Reading Accuracy: ________% **Circle: Fall Winter Spring**
Oral Reading Fluency Score: ____________ **words correct per minute**
Prosody Rubric: (Circle Score) 1 2 3 4
Comprehension Question Responses
#1 ______________________________
#2 ______________________________

The White House

	The White House is the home of the President
9	of the United States. It is indeed a big, white house.
20	A painter would need 570 gallons of white paint to
30	cover all the outside walls!
35	The White House has 6 floors, 132 rooms,
43	and 32 bathrooms. Some rooms are for the
51	President's family and friends. Other rooms are
58	used as offices or for meetings. Parties and other
67	celebrations are held in some rooms. The biggest
75	room is the East Room. It is used for balls and
86	parties. The President has small dinners in the
94	Blue Room. Big dinners, on the other hand, take
103	place in the State Dining Room.
109	You would enjoy a visit to the White House.
118	The tour takes you to five of the rooms. You might
129	even meet the President! **133**

Number of words read: __________ **Number of errors made:** __________

A Birthday Party

Molly turned eight on Sunday. She did not expect a party because she knew her mom had millions of other things to do. But that morning her mom told Molly that they should take a walk in the park. When they got there, Molly saw her closest friends. Five girls and three boys all shouted, "Happy birthday!" Molly was really surprised. Her mom had planned everything. There were snacks. There were games to play. There was even a cake with eight candles.

After eating yummy snacks, the friends played games. Jack won a prize for making a funny face. Kate won a balloon for blowing the biggest bubble. Grace won marbles for hopping on one foot. Everyone got stickers just because they took part in a game.

Then the kids sang to Molly. She blew out the candles and everyone ate cake. Molly was so happy. She thanked all her friends for making her birthday special. She hugged and kissed her mom for giving her the best birthday ever.

1. Name two things that Molly did at her birthday party.
2. Why did Molly's mom suggest that they walk in the park?

Oral Fluency Record Sheet

Name ________________________ Date ____________

Oral Reading Accuracy: ________% Circle: Fall Winter Spring
Oral Reading Fluency Score: ____________ words correct per minute
Prosody Rubric: (Circle Score) 1 2 3 4
Comprehension Question Responses
#1 ________________________
#2 ________________________

A Birthday Party

	Molly turned eight on Sunday. She did not expect
9	a party because she knew her mom had millions of other
20	things to do. But that morning her mom told Molly that
31	they should take a walk in the park. When they got there,
43	Molly saw her closest friends. Five girls and three boys
53	all shouted, "Happy birthday!" Molly was really
60	surprised. Her mom had planned everything. There
67	were snacks. There were games to play. There was
76	even a cake with eight candles.
82	After eating yummy snacks, the friends
88	played games. Jack won a prize for making a funny
98	face. Kate won a balloon for blowing the biggest
107	bubble. Grace won marbles for hopping on one foot.
116	Everyone got stickers just because they took part
124	in a game.
127	Then the kids sang to Molly. She blew out the
137	candles and everyone ate cake. Molly was so
145	happy. She thanked all her friends for making her
154	birthday special. She hugged and kissed her
161	mom for giving her the best birthday ever. **169**

Number of words read: ________ Number of errors made: ________

Fossils

Dinosaurs lived on Earth millions of years ago. Today we know a lot about them. How do we know so much? We learned about them from people who study the remains of dead plants and animals.

Fossils is the name we give to remains that have become hard and turned to stone. Not every plant or animal becomes a fossil when it dies. Some just dry up under the sun. Strong winds blow away others.

For a dead plant or animal to become a fossil, everything must be just right. Sand or mud has to cover the animal or plant quickly. That way, neither the wind nor the sun can destroy it. Then the sand or mud cover turns hard as a rock. Over time, the fossil takes shape.

To find fossils, we must dig for them. We might find a bone, a tooth, or part of a plant. We might even find a footprint! Every find is a clue that tells a little more about life many years ago.

1. How do people find fossils?
2. Why are the sun and the wind a problem when creating new fossils?

Oral Fluency Record Sheet

Name ______________________________ Date ____________

Oral Reading Accuracy: ________% **Circle: Fall Winter Spring**

Oral Reading Fluency Score: ____________ **words correct per minute**

Prosody Rubric: (Circle Score) 1 2 3 4

Comprehension Question Responses

#1 ______________________________

#2 ______________________________

Fossils

	Dinosaurs lived on Earth millions of years
7	ago. Today we know a lot about them. How do we
18	know so much? We learned about them from people
27	who study the remains of dead plants and animals.
36	Fossils is the name we give to remains that
45	have become hard and turned to stone. Not every
54	plant or animal becomes a fossil when it dies.
63	Some just dry up under the sun. Strong winds blow
73	away others.
75	For a dead plant or animal to become a fossil,
85	everything must be just right. Sand or mud has to
95	cover the animal or plant quickly. That way, neither
104	the wind nor the sun can destroy it. Then the sand or
116	mud cover turns hard as a rock. Over time, the fossil
127	takes shape.
129	To find fossils, we must dig for them. We might
139	find a bone, a tooth, or part of a plant. We might even
152	find a footprint! Every find is a clue that tells a little
164	more about life many years ago. **170**

Number of words read: ____________ **Number of errors made:** ____________

Basketball on Wheels

Basketball is a challenging sport to play. Players need strength to move up and down the court and bounce the ball while they are on the move. They also need to be alert for the opportunity to pass. Basketball players cannot relax or let their attention stray for a second. People who play basketball work as a team and depend on each other for support. The same is true for people who play basketball from wheelchairs.

The United States has many basketball teams for children in wheelchairs. The children on these teams bounce the ball, pass, and shoot from their wheelchairs. They learn to move quickly in their chairs and keep track of the ball. They must also be good at passing and shooting. They need a lot of balance, energy, and upper-body strength. Just think how high the basketball hoop looks when you are sitting down.

Wheelchair basketball is an excellent way for children in wheelchairs to be on a team. These players show us we can all be strong if we make the effort.

1. Name three things that are needed by all kinds of basketball players.
2. Why is it important for children in wheelchairs to get the chance to play basketball?

Oral Fluency Record Sheet

Name ______________________________ Date ______________

Oral Reading Accuracy: ________% **Circle:** Fall Winter Spring
Oral Reading Fluency Score: ____________ words correct per minute
Prosody Rubric: (Circle Score) 1 2 3 4
Comprehension Question Responses
#1 ______________________________
#2 ______________________________

Basketball on Wheels

	Basketball is a challenging sport to play. Players need
9	strength to move up and down the court and bounce the ball while
22	they are on the move. They also need to be alert for the opportunity
36	to pass. Basketball players cannot relax or let their attention stray
47	for a second. People who play basketball work as a team and
59	depend on each other for support. The same is true for people who
72	play basketball from wheelchairs.
76	The United States has many basketball teams for
84	children in wheelchairs. The children on these teams bounce
93	the ball, pass, and shoot from their wheelchairs. They learn to
104	move quickly in their chairs and keep track of the ball. They
116	must also be good at passing and shooting. They need a lot of
129	balance, energy, and upper-body strength. Just think how
138	high the basketball hoop looks when you are sitting down.
148	Wheelchair basketball is an excellent way for children
156	in wheelchairs to be on a team. These players show us we can
169	all be strong if we make the effort. **177**

Number of words read: __________ **Number of errors made:** __________

The Pet Rock

Emma still has the pet rock she received for her birthday five years ago. It is still one of her favorite possessions. It is gray with fuzzy orange feet and a lavender tail. Its eyes are outlined in blue and white crayon, and its mouth is drawn in red crayon.

Rob brought the pet rock to Emma's birthday party when she turned six. It was wrapped in a huge yellow box with an enormous bright red bow. When Emma opened the box, she found another box inside wrapped in sparkly green paper. Inside that box was another box wrapped in pink tissue paper. Finally, inside that box was her pet rock.

It was the best gift Emma got that year and the only one she still has from her sixth birthday. It was special and different because Rob had made it himself.

Emma keeps it on a shelf in her room next to the trophy she won at last year's swim competition. When Emma looks at the rock, she remembers Rob, her party that year, and what friendship really means. It is still one of her best memories.

1. Why was Rob's gift so special and different?
2. What was unusual about the way the pet rock was wrapped?

Oral Fluency Record Sheet

Name ______________________________ Date ______________

Oral Reading Accuracy: ________% **Circle: Fall Winter Spring**
Oral Reading Fluency Score: ____________ **words correct per minute**
Prosody Rubric: (Circle Score) 1 2 3 4
Comprehension Question Responses
#1 ____
#2 ____

The Pet Rock

	Emma still has the pet rock she received for her
10	birthday five years ago. It is still one of her favorite
21	possessions. It is gray with fuzzy orange feet and a
31	lavender tail. Its eyes are outlined in blue and white crayon,
42	and its mouth is drawn in red crayon.
50	Rob brought the pet rock to Emma's birthday party
59	when she turned six. It was wrapped in a huge yellow box
71	with an enormous bright red bow. When Emma opened the
81	box, she found another box inside wrapped in sparkly green
91	paper. Inside that box was another box wrapped in pink
101	tissue paper. Finally, inside that box was her pet rock.
111	It was the best gift Emma got that year and the only
123	one she still has from her sixth birthday. It was special and
135	different because Rob had made it himself.
142	Emma keeps it on a shelf in her room next to the
154	trophy she won at last year's swim competition. When
163	Emma looks at the rock, she remembers Rob, her party that
174	year, and what friendship really means. It is still one of
185	her best memories. **188**

Number of words read: __________ **Number of errors made:** __________

The Giant Panda

The giant panda is an animal with a chubby, black-and-white body and black legs. Its head is large and round, and its white face has black patches around each eye.

Panda cubs are extremely tiny when they are born, weighing only about 5 ounces. As adults, however, giant pandas can weigh as much as 350 pounds.

Giant pandas live only in places where there are bamboo forests with plenty of bamboo shoots for them to eat. Because of this, they are found only on high mountain slopes in western and southwestern China. Giant pandas can spend 16 hours a day eating. In one year, a panda can eat more than 10,000 pounds of bamboo. Although the giant panda eats chiefly bamboo shoots, it sometimes eats other plants, fish, and small animals, too.

As a special gift to the people of the United States, China gave two giant pandas to a national zoo in Washington, D.C., in 1972. The pandas lived there for many years, eating bamboo shoots and making all of the zoo visitors laugh.

1. Where do giant pandas live?
2. Why were the giant pandas from China a good gift?

Oral Fluency Record Sheet

Name ______________________ Date ____________

Oral Reading Accuracy: __________% Circle: Fall Winter Spring
Oral Reading Fluency Score: ______________ words correct per minute
Prosody Rubric: (Circle Score) 1 2 3 4
Comprehension Question Responses
#1 ______________________________
#2 ______________________________

The Giant Panda

	The giant panda is an animal with a chubby, black-
10	and-white body and black legs. Its head is large and round,
22	and its white face has black patches around each eye.
32	Panda cubs are extremely tiny when they are born,
41	weighing only about 5 ounces. As adults, however, giant
50	pandas can weigh as much as 350 pounds.
58	Giant pandas live only in places where there are
67	bamboo forests with plenty of bamboo shoots for them to eat.
78	Because of this, they are found only on high mountain
88	slopes in western and southwestern China. Giant pandas
96	can spend 16 hours a day eating. In one year, a panda can
109	eat more than 10,000 pounds of bamboo. Although the
118	giant panda eats chiefly bamboo shoots, it sometimes eats
127	other plants, fish, and small animals, too.
134	As a special gift to the people of the United States,
145	China gave two giant pandas to a national zoo in
155	Washington, D.C., in 1972. The pandas lived there for many
165	years, eating bamboo shoots and making all of the zoo
175	visitors laugh. **177**

Number of words read: __________ **Number of errors made:** __________

One Birthday for All

Every family has traditions. Traditions are things people do year after year. Beth King's family has many traditions they celebrate, but Beth's favorite tradition is about birthdays.

Because Beth has so many aunts, uncles, and cousins, it is impossible to celebrate each birthday. So once a year, on the third Saturday in July, Beth's relatives have one big birthday celebration for everyone. The adults stay at Beth's grandparents' house. The children sleep in tents on the lawn.

Everyone brings food and every meal is a feast. The cousins play soccer. Grandpa and the uncles sit on the wide porch and drink homemade lemonade. The aunts have a softball game. Everyone roots for their favorite team.

Afterwards, everyone eats hamburgers and fresh corn. At the end, Grandma brings out a big frosted cake.

Every year, after the family birthday celebration, Beth goes to bed and starts thinking about next year's birthday party.

1. What is Beth's favorite family tradition?
2. Why does the family have their birthday celebration in the summer?

Oral Fluency Record Sheet

Name ______________________ Date ______________

Oral Reading Accuracy: ________% **Circle: Fall Winter Spring**
Oral Reading Fluency Score: ____________ **words correct per minute**
Prosody Rubric: (Circle Score) 1 2 3 4
Comprehension Question Responses
#1 ______________________________
#2 ______________________________

One Birthday for All

	Every family has traditions. Traditions are things
7	people do year after year. Beth King's family has many
17	traditions they celebrate, but Beth's favorite tradition is
25	about birthdays.
27	Because Beth has so many aunts, uncles, and
35	cousins, it is impossible to celebrate each birthday.
43	So once a year, on the third Saturday in July, Beth's
54	relatives have one big birthday celebration for everyone.
62	The adults stay at Beth's grandparents' house. The
70	children sleep in tents on the lawn.
77	Everyone brings food and every meal is a feast.
86	The cousins play soccer. Grandpa and the uncles sit
95	on the wide porch and drink homemade lemonade.
103	The aunts have a softball game. Everyone roots for their
113	favorite team.
115	Afterwards, everyone eats hamburgers and fresh
121	corn. At the end, Grandma brings out a big frosted cake.
132	Every year, after the family birthday celebration,
139	Beth goes to bed and starts thinking about next year's
149	birthday party. **151**

Number of words read: __________ **Number of errors made:** __________

Ruiz's Toy Chest

Ruiz is almost nine, and he has decided that he has outgrown his old toys. He goes to his toy chest and empties out all his old playthings. His wooden helicopter, some coloring books, his stuffed giraffe, his parrot puppet, and all his other old toys are spread around him on the floor.

"I'll bet the little kid next door would really enjoy playing with some of this stuff," Ruiz thinks to himself as he looks at all of his old toys.

Ruiz picks up his stuffed giraffe with its black nose, orange stripes, long neck, and funny feet. He remembers how he used to pretend he was on the grassy plains of Africa riding on his giraffe.

"Maybe I'll keep my giraffe after all," thinks Ruiz, and he puts the giraffe back into the toy chest.

Ruiz peers into the toy chest. "My giraffe looks really lonely in there," he thinks. "I'd better put the other toys back in so that he'll have some more company."

Ruiz collects all the other toys and puts them back into the toy chest. "I think I'll keep all these old friends a little bit longer," he says to himself.

1. Why does Ruiz plan to give away his old toys?
2. Why does Ruiz decide to keep his old giraffe?

Oral Fluency Record Sheet

Name ______________________ Date ____________

Oral Reading Accuracy: ________% Circle: Fall Winter Spring
Oral Reading Fluency Score: __________ words correct per minute
Prosody Rubric: (Circle Score) 1 2 3 4
Comprehension Question Responses
#1 ______________________
#2 ______________________

Ruiz's Toy Chest

	Ruiz is almost nine, and he has decided that he
10	has outgrown his old toys. He goes to his toy chest
21	and empties out all his old playthings. His wooden
30	helicopter, some coloring books, his stuffed giraffe,
37	his parrot puppet, and all his other old toys are spread
48	around him on the floor.
53	"I'll bet the little kid next door would really
62	enjoy playing with some of this stuff," Ruiz thinks to
72	himself as he looks at all of his old toys.
82	Ruiz picks up his stuffed giraffe with its black
91	nose, orange stripes, long neck, and funny feet. He
100	remembers how he used to pretend he was on the
110	grassy plains of Africa riding on his giraffe.
118	"Maybe I'll keep my giraffe after all," thinks
126	Ruiz, and he puts the giraffe back into the toy chest.
137	Ruiz peers into the toy chest. "My giraffe
145	looks really lonely in there," he thinks. "I'd better put
155	the other toys back in so that he'll have some
165	more company."
167	Ruiz collects all the other toys and puts them
176	back into the toy chest. "I think I'll keep all these old
188	friends a little bit longer," he says to himself. **197**

Number of words read: __________ Number of errors made: __________

Bill Peet, Writer and Artist

Bill Peet is a popular children's writer and artist. Many of his books have animal characters because he loved to draw animals. The animals act like people and were often like people Bill Peet knew.

Before he began writing children's books, Bill Peet wrote and drew illustrations for the movies. He worked on famous films like *Peter Pan* and *Sleeping Beauty.*

Many of Bill Peet's books are very funny, but at the same time they talk about serious problems. In his book *Farewell to Shady Glade,* a group of animals has to leave its home because people want to put up buildings where they live. The animals lose their home, and the reader doesn't know if they will find a new one.

Other books give lessons about life. The book *Kermit the Hermit* is about a selfish crab. After a boy rescues him, Kermit learns that it is important to share.

Through Bill Peet's books, both children and adults get to see the world through new eyes. They get to laugh, but at the same time they get to learn important lessons about life.

1. Who is Bill Peet?
2. Why is Bill Peet an important writer?

Oral Fluency Record Sheet

Name ______________________________ Date ______________

Oral Reading Accuracy: ________% **Circle: Fall Winter Spring**
Oral Reading Fluency Score: ______________ **words correct per minute**
Prosody Rubric: (Circle Score) 1 2 3 4
Comprehension Question Responses
#1 ______________________________
#2 ______________________________

Bill Peet, Writer and Artist

	Bill Peet is a popular children's writer and
8	artist. Many of his books have animal characters
16	because he loved to draw animals. The animals act like
26	people and were often like people Bill Peet knew.
35	Before he began writing children's books, Bill Peet
43	wrote and drew illustrations for the movies. He worked
52	on famous films like *Peter Pan* and *Sleeping Beauty.*
61	Many of Bill Peet's books are very funny, but at
71	the same time they talk about serious problems. In his
81	book *Farewell to Shady Glade,* a group of animals has to
92	leave its home because people want to put up buildings
102	where they live. The animals lose their home, and the
112	reader doesn't know if they will find a new one.
122	Other books give lessons about life. The book
130	*Kermit the Hermit* is about a selfish crab. After a boy
141	rescues him, Kermit learns that it is important
149	to share.
151	Through Bill Peet's books, both children and
158	adults get to see the world through new eyes. They get to
170	laugh, but at the same time they get to learn important
181	lessons about life. **184**

Number of words read: __________ **Number of errors made:** __________

Deep Sleep

Making it through the winter is hard for many animals. Some animals and insects, like birds and butterflies, are able to migrate to warmer places. Other animals, such as bears, cannot make such a far move.

To survive the icy weather, many bears go to sleep. This sleep is called hibernation. Preparing for this deep sleep keeps bears busy throughout late summer and fall. During this time, they must eat a lot of berries and fish. The food helps them gain at least 40 pounds a week. They must store enough body fat because they have to live off this fat while asleep.

For its long sleep, a bear finds a cave or hollow log. Its heart rate may drop from 40 to 10 beats a minute. Most bears start hibernating in early October. When they wake up around April or May, they are very hungry. Be very careful if you know there are bears near where you are living. You would not want to be in the path of a hungry bear.

1. Why do bears sleep during the winter?
2. Why are bears especially dangerous in the spring?

Oral Fluency Record Sheet

Name ______________________ Date ______________

Oral Reading Accuracy: ________% **Circle: Fall Winter Spring**

Oral Reading Fluency Score: ____________ **words correct per minute**

Prosody Rubric: (Circle Score) 1 2 3 4

Comprehension Question Responses

#1 ______________________________

#2 ______________________________

Deep Sleep

	Making it through the winter is hard for many animals. Some
11	animals and insects, like birds and butterflies, are able to migrate to
23	warmer places. Other animals, such as bears, cannot make such a
34	far move.
36	To survive the icy weather, many bears go to sleep. This sleep
48	is called hibernation. Preparing for this deep sleep keeps bears busy
59	throughout late summer and fall. During this time, they must eat a lot
72	of berries and fish. The food helps them gain at least 40 pounds a
86	week. They must store enough body fat because they have to live off
99	this fat while asleep.
103	For its long sleep, a bear finds a cave or hollow log. Its heart
117	rate may drop from 40 to 10 beats a minute. Most bears start
130	hibernating in early October. When they wake up around April or
141	May, they are very hungry. Be very careful if you know there are bears
155	near where you are living. You would not want to be in the path
169	of a hungry bear. **173**

Number of words read: ________ **Number of errors made:** ________

How Skunk Got His Stripes

Skunk did not always have white stripes. Long ago, he was all black. He was black from the tip of his nose to the end of his tail. At night, this was a big problem for the other animals. They could not see Skunk coming.

"We have to solve this problem!" said Bobcat. Skunk had sprayed him just the night before with his scent.

"It is not my fault," said Skunk. "You animals come crashing through my home in the middle of the night. You scare me half to death. What do you expect me to do?"

"I have an idea," said Fawn shyly. Everyone turned to the youngster in surprise. "Perhaps we should give Skunk white spots like mine. Then we could see him in the dark."

Even Skunk thought this was a fine solution. So Bobcat borrowed a bucket of white paint from a farmer's barn. Squirrel said he would paint spots on Skunk.

Squirrel started painting Skunk's back. But then he came to Skunk's tail. He saw that his tail was too bushy for polka dots. The animals decided that stripes would work just as well. And to this day, all skunks have striped tails.

1. What problem were the animals trying to solve?
2. What was Squirrel's solution?

Oral Fluency Record Sheet

Name ______________________________ Date ______________

Oral Reading Accuracy: __________% Circle: Fall Winter Spring
Oral Reading Fluency Score: ______________ words correct per minute
Prosody Rubric: (Circle Score) 1 2 3 4
Comprehension Question Responses
#1 ______________________________
#2 ______________________________

How Skunk Got His Stripes

	Skunk did not always have white stripes. Long ago, he
10	was all black. He was black from the tip of his nose to the end
25	of his tail. At night, this was a big problem for the other
38	animals. They could not see Skunk coming.
45	"We have to solve this problem!" said Bobcat. Skunk
54	had sprayed him just the night before with his scent.
64	"It is not my fault," said Skunk. "You animals come
74	crashing through my home in the middle of the night. You
85	scare me half to death. What do you expect me to do?"
97	"I have an idea," said Fawn shyly. Everyone turned to
107	the youngster in surprise. "Perhaps we should give Skunk
116	white spots like mine. Then we could see him in the dark."
128	Even Skunk thought this was a fine solution. So Bobcat
138	borrowed a bucket of white paint from a farmer's barn.
148	Squirrel said he would paint spots on Skunk.
156	Squirrel started painting Skunk's back. But then he
164	came to Skunk's tail. He saw that his tail was too bushy for
177	polka dots. The animals decided that stripes would work just as
188	well. And to this day, all skunks have striped tails. **198**

Number of words read: __________ **Number of errors made:** __________

Play Ball

What do baseball players need? To start with, they need a bat and ball. A baseball bat is long and round. Most bats are made of ash wood. The bat cannot be longer than 46 inches. It cannot be thicker than $2\frac{3}{4}$ inches at any point. A baseball is small, hard, and round. It weighs about 5 ounces. It has a tiny cork ball at the center. Layers of rubber and yarn are tightly wrapped around this ball. The cover of the ball is made of two pieces of white cowhide. These are sewn together with thick red thread.

Next, players need a special padded leather glove. They also need shoes with spikes on the soles. The spikes help them stop and start quickly.

At bat, players wear a batting helmet. This is a special hard cap. The helmet protects batters in case they are hit in the head with the ball.

In baseball, a pitcher pitches the ball to a catcher. Catchers have special equipment to protect them. They wear a metal mask over their faces. They also wear padded cloth covers over their chests. To protect their legs, they wear hard shin guards.

Baseball can be safe and fun. Are you ready to play ball?

1. What is a baseball made of?
2. Why do baseball players wear special clothing?

Oral Fluency Record Sheet

Name ______________________________ Date ______________

Oral Reading Accuracy: __________% **Circle: Fall Winter Spring**
Oral Reading Fluency Score: ______________ **words correct per minute**
Prosody Rubric: (Circle Score) 1 2 3 4
Comprehension Question Responses
#1 ____
#2 ____

Play Ball

	What do baseball players need? To start with, they need a
11	bat and a ball. A baseball bat is a long and round. Most bats are
26	made of ash wood. The bat cannot be longer than 46 inches. It
39	cannot be thicker than $2\frac{3}{4}$ inches at any point. A baseball is
51	small, hard, and round. It weighs about 5 ounces. It has a tiny cork
65	ball at the center. Layers of rubber and yarn are tightly wrapped
77	around this ball. The cover of the ball is made of two pieces of
91	white cowhide. These are sewn together with thick red thread.
101	Next, players need a special padded leather glove. They also
111	need shoes with spikes on the soles. The spikes help them stop and
124	start quickly.
126	At bat, players wear a batting helmet. This is a special hard
138	cap. The helmet protects batters in case they are hit in the head
151	with the ball.
154	In baseball, a pitcher pitches the ball to a catcher. Catchers
165	have special equipment to protect them. They wear a metal mask
176	over their faces. They also wear padded cloth covers over their
187	chests. To protect their legs, they wear hard shin guards.
197	Baseball can be safe and fun. Are you ready to play ball? **209**

Number of words read: __________ **Number of errors made:** __________

Climbing the Walls

Jill's dad loved rock climbing. He took many trips to the mountains. He wanted Jill to come with him. But first Jill had to learn about climbing.

Jill was excited. She and her dad found a climbing wall in town. Jill put on a helmet and climbing shoes. Then she put on ropes and other gear. Jill's ropes were fastened to the floor. From there, they went around her dad's waist. Then, they went up to the top of the wall.

"I will hold the rope tight," her dad said. "You will be safe. Just go slowly."

Jill looked up at the wall. She saw places for her hands and feet. The top looked far away.

Jill started up. She went from spot to spot. She reached out with her hands. She pushed hard with her feet. At last, she was near the top.

"I can't climb this last bit," she called down.

"Just try," her dad called back. "I'm holding you."

Jill took hold of something small with her hand. She bent down. Then she jumped. Her hand felt the top of the wall. She pulled herself up. She had made it.

"Will you ever do that again?" asked her dad after Jill got back down.

"Oh, yes!" said Jill. "That was great!"

1. What is this story mostly about?
2. Do you think Jill felt safe the whole time she was climbing? Why?

Oral Fluency Record Sheet

Name ______________________________ Date ______________

Oral Reading Accuracy: __________% **Circle: Fall Winter Spring**

Oral Reading Fluency Score: ______________ **words correct per minute**

Prosody Rubric: (Circle Score) 1 2 3 4

Comprehension Question Responses

#1 ______________________________

#2 ______________________________

Climbing the Walls

	Jill's dad loved rock climbing. He took many trips to the
11	mountains. He wanted Jill to come with him. But first Jill had to
24	learn about climbing.
27	Jill was excited. She and her dad found a climbing wall in
39	town. Jill put on a helmet and climbing shoes. Then she put on
52	ropes and other gear. Jill's ropes were fastened to the floor. From
64	there, they went around her dad's waist. Then, they went up to the
77	top of the wall.
81	"I will hold the rope tight," her dad said. "You will be safe.
94	Just go slowly."
97	Jill looked up at the wall. She saw places for her hands and
110	feet. The top looked far away.
116	Jill started up. She went from spot to spot. She reached out
128	with her hands. She pushed hard with her feet. At last, she was
141	near the top.
144	"I can't climb this last bit," she called down.
153	"Just try," her dad called back. "I'm holding you."
162	Jill took hold of something small with her hand. She bent
173	down. Then she jumped. Her hand felt the top of the wall. She
186	pulled herself up. She had made it.
193	"Will you ever do that again?" asked her dad after Jill got
205	back down.
207	"Oh, yes!" said Jill. "That was great!" **214**

Number of words read: __________ **Number of errors made:** __________

Up, Up, and Away

For thousands of years, people dreamed of flying. They tried many things. Nothing seemed to work.

Then in 1783, two brothers in France got a new idea. They were watching smoke. They noticed the way smoke moves up from a fire. It does not seem to come back down. The brothers filled paper bags with smoke. They watched as the smoke moved the bags into the air.

The brothers decided to make a big balloon. They filled it with smoke. When it was full, they let it go. Up, up it went.

Next, the brothers built another balloon. This time they attached a basket to the balloon. In September 1783, they were ready. They put a rooster, a duck, and a sheep in the basket. They filled the balloon with hot air and let it go. Up it went, this time with passengers. Then, high above the earth, the warm air cooled. The balloon floated back to the ground. The three animals had taken a round-trip air flight.

Two other Frenchmen watched these events. They decided to become the first people to fly. They built a big blue and gold balloon. In November 1783, the balloon carried them over the city of Paris.

Today we take air travel for granted. But not too long ago, flight was still a mystery and a challenge.

1. What is this passage mainly about?
2. Explain what makes the balloons rise.

Oral Fluency Record Sheet

Name ______________________________ Date ______________

Oral Reading Accuracy: ________% **Circle: Fall Winter Spring**
Oral Reading Fluency Score: ____________ **words correct per minute**
Prosody Rubric: (Circle Score) 1 2 3 4
Comprehension Question Responses
#1 ______________________________
#2 ______________________________

Up, Up, and Away

	For thousands of years, people dreamed of flying. They
9	tried many things. Nothing seemed to work.
16	Then in 1783, two brothers in France got a new idea. They
28	were watching smoke. They noticed the way smoke moves up
38	from a fire. It does not seem to come back down. The brothers
51	filled paper bags with smoke. They watched as the smoke moved
62	the bags into the air.
67	The brothers decided to make a big balloon. They filled it
78	with smoke. When it was full, they let it go. Up, up it went.
92	Next, the brothers built another balloon. This time they
101	attached a basket to the balloon. In September 1783, they were
112	ready. They put a rooster, a duck, and a sheep in the basket. They
126	filled the balloon with hot air and let it go. Up it went, this time
141	with passengers. Then, high above the earth, the warm air cooled.
152	The balloon floated back to the ground. The three animals had
163	taken a round-trip air flight.
169	Two other Frenchmen watched these events. They decided
177	to become the first people to fly. They built a big blue and gold
191	balloon. In November 1983, the balloon carried them over the city
202	of Paris.
204	Today we take air travel for granted. But not too long ago,
216	flight was still a mystery and a challenge. **224**

Number of words read: __________ **Number of errors made:** __________

The Great Wall of China

One of the wonders of the world stands in China. It is the Great Wall of China. The Great Wall is the longest structure ever built. It is about 4,600 miles long.

The Chinese built the wall as protection against enemies. It was started more than 2,500 years ago. Workers made big piles of dirt. They pounded the dirt until it was very hard. They would use this hard dirt to build the wall. Over time the wall crumbled. It was rebuilt again and again.

Often, the wall did not work. For example, in the 1200s, enemies climbed over it to conquer China.

Today, people see the wall that went up between 1368 and 1644. This wall went up during the Ming Dynasty. At first, the Ming built the old way. They piled and pounded dirt. But rain and wind destroyed these walls. The builders turned to stone and brick. These walls took longer to build. They cost more, too. But they lasted longer.

The new wall had towers. Soldiers lived in some of them. They sent signals from others. For signals, they built fires. They used smoke during the day. At night they used flames. People far away could get ready for an attack.

Today, the wall is crumbling. No one knows how much longer it will stand. Rain and wind break parts of the wall. Some people take bricks. Others write on the wall. The wall once protected China. Now China must protect the wall.

1. What is special about the Great Wall of China?
2. Why was the Great Wall built?

Oral Fluency Record Sheet

Name ______________________________ Date ______________

Oral Reading Accuracy: ________% **Circle: Fall Winter Spring**

Oral Reading Fluency Score: ____________ **words correct per minute**

Prosody Rubric: (Circle Score) 1 2 3 4

Comprehension Question Responses

#1 ______________________________

#2 ______________________________

The Great Wall of China

	One of the wonders of the world stands in China. It is the
13	Great Wall of China. The Great Wall is the longest structure ever
25	built. It is about 4,600 miles long.
32	The Chinese built the wall as protection against enemies. It
42	was started more than 2,500 years ago. Workers made big piles of
54	dirt. They pounded the dirt until it was very hard. They would
66	use this hard dirt to build the wall. Over time the wall crumbled.
79	It was rebuilt again and again.
85	Often, the wall did not work. For example, in the 1200s,
96	enemies climbed over it to conquer China.
103	Today, people see the wall that went up between 1368
113	and 1644. This wall went up during the Ming Dynasty. At
124	first, the Ming built the old way. They piled and pounded dirt. But
137	rain and wind destroyed these walls. The builders turned to stone
148	and brick. These walls took longer to build. They cost more, too.
160	But they lasted longer.
164	The new wall had towers. Soldiers lived in some of them.
175	They sent signals from others. For signals, they built fires. They
186	used smoke during the day. At night they used flames. People far
198	away could get ready for an attack.
205	Today, the wall is crumbling. No one knows how much
215	longer it will stand. Rain and wind break parts of the wall. Some
228	people take bricks. Others write on the wall. The wall once
239	protected China. Now China must protect the wall. **247**

Number of words read: __________ **Number of errors made:** __________

The Little Brother

Anna thought her little brother was a real pest. He sat on her bed while she gossiped on the telephone. He watched her as she did her homework. He sat on the floor at her feet as she watched TV. Matt was three years old. Anna knew he loved her. She loved him, too, but enough was enough.

One afternoon, Anna was sitting at her tiny desk in the corner of the family room. She was trying to finish her math homework. Matt kept asking her questions about the spiral notebook she was using. He also wanted to know about the numbers that she was writing. And why, he asked, did she use her eraser so often? Finally, Anna pleaded with her mother for some help. She just wanted some peace and quiet.

Anna's mother smiled. Then she asked Anna if she would like it if her friends always shooed her away. Anna suddenly saw that Matt was her friend, as well as her brother. She gave him a crayon and a piece of notebook paper. Then she made room for him at her desk.

1. What did Anna's little brother do to annoy her?
2. How did Anna's mother help her see her brother differently?

Oral Fluency Record Sheet

Name ____________________ Date ____________

Oral Reading Accuracy: _______%
Oral Reading Fluency Score: __________ words correct per minute
Prosody Rubric: (Circle Score) 1 2 3 4
Comprehension Question Responses
#1 ____________________
#2 ____________________

The Little Brother

	Anna thought her little brother was a real pest. He sat on
12	her bed while she gossiped on the telephone. He watched her as
24	she did her homework. He sat on the floor at her feet as she
38	watched TV. Matt was three years old. Anna knew he loved her.
50	She loved him, too, but enough was enough.
58	One afternoon, Anna was sitting at her tiny desk in the
69	corner of the family room. She was trying to finish her math
81	homework. Matt kept asking her questions about the spiral
90	notebook she was using. He also wanted to know about the
101	numbers that she was writing. And why, he asked, did she use
113	her eraser so often? Finally, Anna pleaded with her mother for
124	some help. She just wanted some peace and quiet.
133	Anna's mother smiled. Then she asked Anna if she would
143	like it if her friends always shooed her away. Anna suddenly saw
155	that Matt was her friend, as well as her brother. She gave him a
169	crayon and a piece of notebook paper. Then she made room for
181	him at her desk. **185**

Number of words read: ________ **Number of errors made:** ________

Moons

Many years ago, Native Americans did not have calendars to tell them what month or day it was. Instead, they had the moon. By keeping track of the time it took for the moon to go from one full moon phase to the next, they measured their days.

Each phase was called a moon, and each moon was about the length of a month. During a moon, the Native Americans looked at leaves on the trees. They noted how cold the winds were, and what the Earth looked like around them. They observed what color the rabbits' fur was, and if choke cherries were on the bushes. Then they named that moon phase for what they saw and felt.

March might be the Moon of the Long Rains to a Native American living in the Northeast. To a Native American in a dry climate, March might be the Moon of the Desert Blooms. Moons could also be named after feasts and ceremonies, such as the moon of Summer Encampment. Children learned about the moons from their elders, and looked forward to what each new moon would bring.

1. How did Native Americans keep track of what month or day it was?
2. How did Native Americans decide what to name a moon phase?

Oral Fluency Record Sheet

Name ______________________ Date __________

Oral Reading Accuracy: ________%
Oral Reading Fluency Score: ____________ **words correct per minute**
Prosody Rubric: (Circle Score) 1 2 3 4
Comprehension Question Responses
#1 ______________________
#2 ______________________

Moons

	Many years ago, Native Americans did not have calendars
9	to tell them what month or day it was. Instead, they had the moon.
23	By keeping track of the time it took for the moon to go from one
38	full moon phase to the next, they measured their days.
48	Each phase was called a moon, and each moon was about
59	the length of a month. During a moon, the Native Americans looked at
72	leaves on the trees. They noted how cold the winds were, and what
85	the Earth looked like around them. They observed what color
95	the rabbits' fur was, and if choke cherries were on the bushes.
107	Then they named that moon phase for what they saw and felt.
119	March might be the Moon of the Long Rains to a Native
131	American living in the Northeast. To a Native American in a dry
143	climate, March might be the Moon of the Desert Blooms. Moons
154	could also be named after feasts and ceremonies, such as the
165	moon of Summer Encampment. Children learned about the moons
174	from their elders, and looked forward to what each new moon
185	would bring. **187**

Number of words read: ________ **Number of errors made:** ________

Before and Now

You do not have to be Columbus to be interested in traveling to new places. Many people living today are just as curious as Columbus once was. These brave people leave their beloved homelands behind and move to new countries to live. These people are called *immigrants,* and they show extraordinary courage! Try to imagine leaving everything you know and love behind, and moving to a place you have never even seen before. Perhaps your parents or grandparents did just that. Maybe you are an immigrant yourself.

But what about the countries left behind? What did they look like? If you know any immigrants, ask them if they have any old photographs you can look at. What would you see in those photos? What would the automobiles look like, the buildings, even the clothes the people wore? What would these things tell you about the other place the person had lived? If you do not know anyone who has moved to this country, or you do not have any photos to look at, you can go to your local library. Look up travel books and videos. If you are extremely lucky, you may know someone who kept a diary or journal describing what life was like where they came from. This type of keepsake will help bring the old country and the new one together.

1. What is this passage mostly about?
2. Why might people move to a new country?

Oral Fluency Record Sheet

Name ______________________________ Date ______________

Oral Reading Accuracy: ________%

Oral Reading Fluency Score: __________ **words correct per minute**

Prosody Rubric: (Circle Score) 1 2 3 4

Comprehension Question Responses

#1 ______________________________

#2 ______________________________

Before and Now

	You do not have to be Columbus to be interested
10	in traveling to new places. Many people living today are just
21	as curious as Columbus once was. These brave people leave
31	their beloved homelands behind and move to new countries
40	to live. These people are called *immigrants*, and they show
50	extraordinary courage! Try to imagine leaving everything
57	you know and love behind, and moving to a place you have
69	never even seen before. Perhaps your parents or grandparents
78	did just that. Maybe you are an immigrant yourself.
87	But what about the countries left behind? What did
96	they look like? If you know any immigrants, ask them if they
108	have any old photographs you can look at. What would you
119	see in those photos? What would the automobiles look like,
129	the buildings, even the clothes the people wore? What would
139	these things tell you about the other place the person had
150	lived? If you do not know anyone who has moved to this
162	country, or you do not have any photos to look at, you can
175	go to your local library. Look up travel books and videos.
186	If you are extremely lucky, you may know someone who
196	kept a diary or journal describing what life was like where
207	they came from. This type of keepsake will help bring
217	the old country and the new one together. **225**

Number of words read: __________ **Number of errors made:** __________

Why Winter Comes

Centuries ago, people noticed that Earth was warm and green some of the time and bitter cold at other times. This was a cycle that repeated itself over and over. To explain these changes, ancient people told stories. There were myths to explain just about every cycle in nature. Some stories explained why the sun disappeared each night and reappeared each morning. Other myths told what caused the moon to wax and wane.

Why winter arrived each year is explained in one myth about a Greek goddess named Demeter. The myth said that Demeter had a beautiful daughter named Persephone. Hades, the god of the underworld, snatched Persephone and brought her to his kingdom. Demeter was so depressed by her daughter's sudden disappearance that she caused Earth to become cold and barren. Nothing grew during the time that Persephone was in the underworld.

Demeter begged Hades to return her daughter. Eventually, Hades gave in and allowed the girl to return to her mother. But Demeter had to promise that Persephone would spend part of every year with him. When she saw Persephone again, Demeter was overjoyed, and she allowed plants to grow again.

This was an early explanation of why winter arrived each year. Winter was the time that Persephone had to go back to the underworld.

1. What is the author's purpose for writing this passage?
2. According to this myth, what causes winter?

Oral Fluency Record Sheet

Name ______________________________ Date ______________

Oral Reading Accuracy: __________%

Oral Reading Fluency Score: ______________ **words correct per minute**

Prosody Rubric: (Circle Score) 1 2 3 4

Comprehension Question Responses

#1 ______________________________

#2 ______________________________

Why Winter Comes

	Centuries ago, people noticed that Earth was warm
8	and green some of the time and bitter cold at other times.
20	This was a cycle that repeated itself over and over. To explain
32	these changes, ancient people told stories. There were myths
41	to explain just about every cycle in nature. Some stories
51	explained why the sun disappeared each night and reappeared
60	each morning. Other myths told what caused the moon to
70	wax and wane.
73	Why winter arrived each year is explained in one myth about
84	a Greek goddess named Demeter. The myth said that Demeter
94	had a beautiful daughter named Persephone. Hades, the god of
104	the underworld, snatched Persephone and brought her to his
113	kingdom. Demeter was so depressed by her daughter's sudden
122	disappearance that she caused Earth to become cold and
131	barren. Nothing grew during the time that Persephone was
140	in the underworld.
143	Demeter begged Hades to return her daughter. Eventually,
151	Hades gave in and allowed the girl to return to her mother.
163	But Demeter had to promise that Persephone would spend
172	part of every year with him. When she saw Persephone again,
183	Demeter was overjoyed, and she allowed plants to grow again.
193	This was an early explanation of why winter arrived each
203	year. Winter was the time that Persephone had to go back to
215	the underworld. **217**

Number of words read: __________ **Number of errors made:** __________

Special Eyes

Tim and his family are raising a special puppy named Luke. Luke is a German shepherd. He was born at the guide dog center. With his three brothers and sisters, he will become a guide dog. He will learn how to help blind people.

Guide dogs help blind people cross busy streets. They help them walk inside stores and buy groceries. They help them in restaurants and on buses.

Luke's brothers and sisters are named Lark, Lisa, and Len. Why do all the names begin with the same letter? It helps the center keep track of Luke and the group.

Luke will grow up with Tim and his family. He will learn about riding in cars and living with people. When he is fourteen months old, he will go back to the center. There he will learn to obey commands. He will learn words such as "left," "right," and "sit." He will also learn to keep his mind on his work. Most dogs are distracted by sounds, smells, and other animals. Luke will learn to concentrate on leading his partner.

At Luke's graduation, Tim will meet Luke's new partner. He will be sad to say goodbye. But he will be happy for Luke. He will be a loving helper. His eyes will become special eyes for someone who needs him.

1. What is the role of Tim and his family in Luke's life?
2. What is a guide dog's job mostly about?

Oral Fluency Record Sheet

Name ______________________________________ Date __________________

Oral Reading Accuracy: __________%
Oral Reading Fluency Score: ________________ **words correct per minute**
Prosody Rubric: (Circle Score) 1 2 3 4
Comprehension Question Responses
#1 ____
#2 ____

Special Eyes

	Tim and his family are raising a special puppy named
10	Luke. Luke is a German shepherd. He was born at the guide dog
23	center. With his three brothers and sisters, he will become a
34	guide dog. He will learn how to help blind people.
44	Guide dogs help blind people cross busy streets. They
53	help them walk inside stores and buy groceries. They help them
64	in restaurants and on buses.
69	Luke's brothers and sisters are named Lark, Lisa, and Len.
79	Why do all the names begin with the same letter? It helps the
92	center keep track of Luke and the group.
100	Luke will grow up with Tim and his family. He will learn
112	about riding in cars and living with people. When he is fourteen
124	months old, he will go back to the center. There he will learn to
138	obey commands. He will learn words such as "left," "right," and
149	"sit." He will also learn to keep his mind on his work. Most dogs
163	are distracted by sounds, smells, and other animals. Luke will
173	learn to concentrate on leading his partner.
180	At Luke's graduation, Tim will meet Luke's new partner.
189	He will be sad to say goodbye. But he will be happy for Luke.
203	He will be a loving helper. His eyes will become special eyes
215	for someone who needs him. **220**

Number of words read: __________ **Number of errors made:** __________

The Kite Contest

Jed and his little brother Tom were at the park for the kite contest. The contestant whose kite stayed up the longest would win.

The boys waited to hear their numbers. Kites swooped and soared above them. Some stayed up for a long time. Others dropped to the grass almost immediately. Finally the boys' numbers were called. Jed raced to the open field, but Tom stood still.

"I can't," he mumbled as he dropped his kite.

Jed thought for a moment. Then he went over and picked up Tom's kite. "I'll fly both of them," he said.

Jed began to run, and both kites soared into the sky. Then unexpectedly the wind jerked at Jed's kite, and the kite ripped. "My kite can't fly now," thought Jed. He dropped the string to his kite, and the kite fell to the ground. But he still had Tom's kite. He kept on running.

Suddenly the whistle blew. The contest was over. The boys met near the judge's stand to hear who had won.

"There are three winners," the judge announced. "First place goes to number 21. Second place goes to number 9. Third place goes to number 35."

"Number 35!" Jed shouted. "That's me." He jumped up and ran quickly to the judge.

"You're the one who flew two kites," the judge said. "Great job!" He handed him a green ribbon.

"It was really my brother's kite," Jed said shyly. "I'm going to share this prize with him."

1. What did a contestant need to do to win the contest?
2. What was unusual about the way Jed won his ribbon?

Oral Fluency Record Sheet

Name ____________________ Date ____________

Oral Reading Accuracy: ________%

Oral Reading Fluency Score: ____________ **words correct per minute**

Prosody Rubric: (Circle Score) 1 2 3 4

Comprehension Question Responses

#1 ______________________________

#2 ______________________________

The Kite Contest

	Jed and his little brother Tom were at the park for the kite
13	contest. The contestant whose kite stayed up the longest would win.
24	The boys waited to hear their numbers. Kites swooped and
34	soared above them. Some stayed up for a long time. Others dropped
46	to the grass almost immediately. Finally the boys' numbers were
56	called. Jed raced to the open field, but Tom stood still.
67	"I can't," he mumbled as he dropped his kite.
76	Jed thought for a moment. Then he went over and picked
87	up Tom's kite. "I'll fly both of them," he said.
97	Jed began to run, and both kites soared into the sky. Then
109	unexpectedly the wind jerked at Jed's kite, and the kite ripped. "My
121	kite can't fly now," thought Jed. He dropped the string to his kite,
134	and the kite fell to the ground. But he still had Tom's kite. He kept
149	on running.
151	Suddenly the whistle blew. The contest was over. The boys
161	met near the judge's stand to hear who had won.
171	"There are three winners," the judge announced. "First
179	place goes to number 21. Second place goes to number 9. Third
191	place goes to number 35."
196	"Number 35!" Jed shouted. "That's me." He
203	jumped up and ran quickly to the judge.
211	"You're the one who flew two kites," the judge said. "Great
222	job!" He handed him a green ribbon.
229	"It was really my brother's kite," Jed said shyly. "I'm going
240	to share this prize with him." **246**

Number of words read: ________ **Number of errors made:** ________

When You Snooze, You Lose

Carlos detested getting up in the morning. He rarely felt awake until sometime in the afternoon. By dinnertime, he was prepared for anything. By bedtime, he was unbelievably energized. Unfortunately for Carlos, school starts in the morning.

Carlos's dad resented having to wake him up ten times each morning. So his parents bought Carlos an alarm clock that had an especially loud buzz for an alarm. They informed him that getting up was now his responsibility.

The first morning, the buzz was deafening. Carlos woke up terrified. Then he realized it was simply his new alarm clock. He decided that he did not need such an earsplitting signal. Happily, he lowered the sound level.

The next morning, Carlos continued sleeping through the quiet buzz. He missed breakfast, missed the bus, and had to hustle off to school on his own two legs.

It was raining, but Carlos forgot to close his backpack. His homework got drenched and fell apart in his hands. He also forgot his lunch money as he sprinted out of the apartment. So Carlos had no lunch and then stayed after school to redo his homework. He missed the bus again and plodded home in the drizzling rain.

As soon as Carlos entered his apartment, he raced to his room and turned up the volume on his alarm. Sleeping late was just not worth it.

1. Why did Carlos's parents get him an alarm clock?
2. What lesson did Carlos learn?

Oral Fluency Record Sheet

Name ______________________________ Date ______________

Oral Reading Accuracy: __________%

Oral Reading Fluency Score: ______________ **words correct per minute**

Prosody Rubric: (Circle Score) 1 2 3 4

Comprehension Question Responses

#1 ____

#2 ____

When You Snooze, You Lose

	Carlos detested getting up in the morning. He rarely
9	felt awake until sometime in the afternoon. By dinnertime, he was
20	prepared for anything. By bedtime, he was unbelievably energized.
29	Unfortunately for Carlos, school starts in the morning.
37	Carlos's dad resented having to wake him up ten times
47	each morning. So his parents bought Carlos an alarm clock that had
59	an especially loud buzz for an alarm. They informed him that
70	getting up was now his responsibility.
76	The first morning, the buzz was deafening. Carlos woke up
86	terrified. Then he realized it was simply his new alarm clock. He
98	decided that he did not need such an earsplitting signal. Happily, he
110	lowered the sound level.
114	The next morning, Carlos continued sleeping through the
122	quiet buzz. He missed breakfast, missed the bus, and had to hustle
134	off to school on his own two legs.
142	It was raining, but Carlos forgot to close his backpack. His
153	homework got drenched and fell apart in his hands. He also forgot
165	his lunch money as he sprinted out of the apartment. So Carlos had
178	no lunch and then stayed after school to redo his homework. He
190	missed the bus again and plodded home in the drizzling rain.
201	As soon as Carlos entered his apartment, he raced to his
212	room and turned up the volume on his alarm. Sleeping late was just
225	not worth it. **228**

Number of words read: __________ **Number of errors made:** __________

Mr. Lazy-Bones

Matt Kroger was incredibly lazy. He was so lazy that sometimes at dinnertime he would still be lounging in his pajamas. Putting on regular clothes was too much work, and so was tying shoes, combing hair, or striding up a one-story flight of stairs instead of taking the elevator. Matt focused on avoiding any kind of activity. But Matt loved money, so when Mrs. Tinsley asked him to walk her dog Coco, Matt grabbed the opportunity. Five dollars for a ten-minute walk was a terrific deal.

When he asked me to accompany him, I thought, "Why not? I have nothing better to do anyway."

One dog eventually led to two, because Matt discovered that walking a second pooch was like getting paid double for an identical amount of work. Then we were asked to walk a third and a fourth dog.

While strolling with the dogs, we thought, "Why not take on a paper route as well?"

"It would be like free money," Matt declared. "It won't take us any more time because we have to go around the neighborhood every day anyway."

That's right. We delivered newspapers while we walked the four dogs. Never mind that our ten-minute walk now required an investment of more than an hour. The laziest kid in the universe had become the hardest working one of all.

1. Why did Matt decide to start walking dogs?
2. What lesson did Matt learn in this story?

Oral Fluency Record Sheet

Name ______________________ Date ______________

Oral Reading Accuracy: ________%

Oral Reading Fluency Score: ____________ words correct per minute

Prosody Rubric: (Circle Score) 1 2 3 4

Comprehension Question Responses

#1 ______________________

#2 ______________________

Mr. Lazy-Bones

	Matt Kroger was incredibly lazy. He was so lazy that
10	sometimes at dinnertime he would still be lounging in his pajamas.
21	Putting on regular clothes was too much work, and so was tying
33	shoes, combing hair, or striding up a one-story flight of stairs
45	instead of taking the elevator. Matt focused on avoiding any
55	kind of activity. But Matt loved money, so when Mrs.
65	Tinsley asked him to walk her dog Coco, Matt grabbed the
76	opportunity. Five dollars for a ten-minute walk was a terrific deal.
88	When he asked me to accompany him, I thought, "Why
98	not? I have nothing better to do anyway."
106	One dog eventually led to two, because Matt discovered
115	that walking a second pooch was like getting paid double for an
127	identical amount of work. Then we were asked to walk a third
139	and a fourth dog.
143	While strolling with the dogs, we thought, "Why not take
153	on a paper route as well?"
159	"It would be like free money," Matt declared. "It won't take
170	us any more time because we have to go around the neighborhood
182	every day anyway."
185	That's right. We delivered newspapers while we walked the
194	four dogs. Never mind that our ten-minute walk now required an
206	investment of more than an hour. The laziest kid in the universe
218	had become the hardest working one of all. **226**

Number of words read: __________ **Number of errors made:** __________

Making a Home in a New Place

Every year, millions of people move to the United States from other countries. To move from one country to another is called *immigration*. Immigrants come from all over the world, and they have many different reasons for packing up their belongings and seeking a home in a new country. They may be looking for better jobs, or they may be fleeing from a land where their freedom was denied. Natural disasters may have forced them to leave. Maybe they are looking for the chance to have a better education. Whatever their reasons, they leave behind friends, a way of life, and many memories.

After an immigrant family moves to the United States, they may decide not to stay in the same city they first arrived at. Many immigrants first try to establish themselves near other family members who had immigrated earlier. Sooner or later, the new immigrants may discover that they would have better opportunities elsewhere. They might prefer living in another town, or even another state.

At the beginning of the last century, for instance, many immigrants came from Europe on vessels that landed in New York City. Quite a few of them remained there. But millions of them headed elsewhere, traveling by train, boat, or car.

Today, a family may travel conveniently by plane. However, they still face the same old-fashioned challenge of making a home in a strange place. A family may move a number of times before they eventually find an appropriate place to live.

1. Why do people immigrate?
2. What are some of the decisions new immigrants need to make?

Oral Fluency Record Sheet

Name ______________________________ Date ______________

Oral Reading Accuracy: __________%
Oral Reading Fluency Score: ______________ words correct per minute
Prosody Rubric: (Circle Score) 1 2 3 4
Comprehension Question Responses
#1 ______________________________
#2 ______________________________

Making a Home in a New Place

Every year, millions of people move to the United States from
11 other countries. To move from one country to another is called
22 *immigration.* Immigrants come from all over the world, and they have
33 many different reasons for packing up their belongings and seeking
43 a home in a new country. They may be looking for better jobs, or they
58 may be fleeing from a land where their freedom was denied. Natural
70 disasters may have forced them to leave. Maybe they are looking for the
83 chance to have a better education. Whatever their reasons, they leave
94 behind friends, a way of life, and many memories.
103 After an immigrant family moves to the United States, they
113 may decide not to stay in the same city they first arrived at.
126 Many immigrants first try to establish themselves near other family
136 members who had immigrated earlier. Sooner or later, the new
146 immigrants may discover that they would have better opportunities
155 elsewhere. They might prefer living in another town, or even
165 another state.
167 At the beginning of the last century, for instance, many
177 immigrants came from Europe on vessels that landed in New York
188 City. Quite a few of them remained there. But millions of them
200 headed elsewhere, traveling by train, boat, or car.
208 Today, a family may travel conveniently by plane. However,
217 they still face the same old-fashioned challenge of making a home in
230 a strange place. A family may move a number of times before they
243 eventually find an appropriate place to live. **250**

Number of words read: __________ **Number of errors made:** __________

The Last Frontier

Many people claim that space is the last frontier. By this they mean that every country on Earth has already been discovered and explored. To be true explorers, they say, we must journey to distant planets.

While it may be true that space is an open frontier, plenty of frontier still exists here on our planet. This is because the deepest spots of our planet, deep areas beneath the oceans, are still unexplored. The average depth of the world's oceans is 12,200 feet, but parts of the ocean plunge much deeper. The deepest known spot is in the western Pacific and is 36,198 feet below sea level.

Divers can go only so far with the deep sea breathing equipment we have today. To really reach the ocean's depths, people need to travel in special vehicles especially built for underwater exploration. Only a handful of people have done that.

We know that plant life is rare deep below the ocean's surface. That's because sunlight is necessary for plant survival and solar rays can penetrate only about 660 feet below the surface of the water. Deeper than that, the waters are completely dark and plants are unable to survive. Many sea creatures depend on plants for food. What can we assume then about animal activity in the deep water?

We know that some animals have adapted to life in the dark by becoming luminous, giving off a glow. Other creatures have become scavengers, feeding on whatever drops to the ocean floor. But these are just scattered pieces of information. Perhaps one day you will become an underwater explorer and uncover even more secrets of the deep sea.

1. In the author's opinion, what really is the last frontier?
2. Why don't we know more about life at the bottom of the ocean?

Oral Fluency Record Sheet

Name ______________________ Date ______________

Oral Reading Accuracy: ____________%
Oral Reading Fluency Score: ______________ words correct per minute
Prosody Rubric: (Circle Score) 1 2 3 4
Comprehension Question Responses
#1 ______________________
#2 ______________________

The Last Frontier

	Many people claim that space is the last frontier. By this
11	they mean that every country on Earth has already been discovered
22	and explored. To be true explorers, they say, we must journey to
34	distant planets.
36	While it may be true that space is an open frontier, plenty
48	of frontier still exists here on our planet. This is because the
60	deepest spots of our planet, deep areas beneath the oceans, are still
72	unexplored. The average depth of the world's oceans is 12,200 feet,
83	but parts of the ocean plunge much deeper. The deepest known
94	spot is in the western Pacific and is 36,198 feet below sea level.
107	Divers can go only so far with the deep sea breathing
118	equipment we have today. To really reach the ocean's depths,
128	people need to travel in special vehicles especially built for
138	underwater exploration. Only a handful of people have done that.
148	We know that plant life is rare deep below the ocean's
159	surface. That's because sunlight is necessary for plant survival and
169	solar rays can penetrate only about 660 feet below the surface of
181	the water. Deeper than that, the waters are completely dark and
192	plants are unable to survive. Many sea creatures depend on plants
203	for food. What can we assume then about animal activity in the
215	deep water?
217	We know that some animals have adapted to life in the dark
229	by becoming luminous, giving off a glow. Other creatures have
239	become scavengers, feeding on whatever drops to the ocean floor.
249	But these are just scattered pieces of information. Perhaps one day
260	you will become an underwater explorer and uncover even more
270	secrets of the deep sea. **275**

Number of words read: ____________ **Number of errors made: ____________**

Odysseus and the Sirens

Odysseus was a distinguished Greek hero celebrated in many legends. One of these legends tells about an adventure Odysseus had while sailing home from Troy.

Odysseus knew that he and his crew would have to pass perilously close to the island of the Sirens. The Sirens were a dangerous group of singers whose voices were extremely beautiful. Every time a ship got close to the island, the Sirens would deliberately stand on a hilltop, waving and singing rhythmically. The ship's crew would forget about steering and head directly for the beautiful melody. Before long, their boat would crash and break against the rocky shore.

Odysseus was a man with common sense. He did not want his boat to be destroyed by the Sirens. He came up with a good plan. He instructed his crew to plug their ears with wax while the ship was steering past the island. Then the crew would not be able to hear the song, and the boat would be safe.

But Odysseus yearned to hear the Siren's song. So he thought of another scheme. He had the crew strap him tightly to the mast. Then, as the crew rowed near the island, Odysseus listened to the most beautiful music imaginable. He struggled in vain to get free, to throw himself into the water and swim toward the Sirens. Finally, the boat passed the island. The sailors took the wax out of their ears and loosened the knots tying Odysseus. He was exhausted, but safe.

1. What danger did Odysseus face near the island of the Sirens?
2. Why did the crew tie Odysseus to the mast?

Oral Fluency Record Sheet

Name ______________________ Date ______________

Oral Reading Accuracy: _________%
Oral Reading Fluency Score: ______________ words correct per minute
Prosody Rubric: (Circle Score) 1 2 3 4
Comprehension Question Responses
#1 ______________________
#2 ______________________

Odysseus and the Sirens

	Odysseus was a distinguished Greek hero celebrated in
8	many legends. One of these legends tells about an adventure
18	Odysseus had while sailing home from Troy.
25	Odysseus knew that he and his crew would have to pass
36	perilously close to the island of the Sirens. The Sirens were a
48	dangerous group of singers whose voices were extremely beautiful.
57	Every time a ship got close to the island, the Sirens would
69	deliberately stand on a hilltop, waving and singing rhythmically.
78	The ship's crew would forget about steering and head directly for
89	the beautiful melody. Before long, their boat would crash and
99	break against the rocky shore.
104	Odysseus was a man with common sense. He did not want
115	his boat to be destroyed by the Sirens. He came up with a good
129	plan. He instructed his crew to plug their ears with wax while the
142	ship was steering past the island. Then the crew would not be able
155	to hear the song, and the boat would be safe.
165	But Odysseus yearned to hear the Siren's song. So he
175	thought of another scheme. He had the crew strap him tightly to
187	the mast. Then, as the crew rowed near the island, Odysseus
198	listened to the most beautiful music imaginable. He struggled in
208	vain to get free, to throw himself into the water and swim toward
221	the Sirens. Finally, the boat passed the island. The sailors took the
233	wax out of their ears and loosened the knots tying Odysseus. He
245	was exhausted, but safe. **249**

Number of words read: __________ Number of errors made: __________

Egyptian Writing

Egyptian picture writing, or hieroglyphics, began almost 5,000 years ago. At first, the Egyptians just drew pictures to stand for objects. For example, the sun was a circle with a dot in it. A house was a small rectangle. Over time, it became too difficult to come up with a new picture for each word. So the Egyptians began to combine words to make sounds. For example, the Egyptian word for "go out" sounds like the words for "house" and "sun." Writers just combined these two pictures when they needed to write the word that means "go out."

Over the centuries, the ability to understand Egyptian writing was lost. Experts puzzled over Egyptian texts without any idea of what they meant. Then, in 1799, an officer in the French army found the Rosetta Stone in Egypt. The strange black stone had three sections of writing carved into it. The first section was a story in Greek. The other two sections were translations of the same story into Egyptian picture writing. Using these translations, experts quickly decoded the Rosetta Stone. Using what they deciphered, they soon solved the puzzle of Egyptian hieroglyphics.

Picture writing was used for thousands of years. But by 1000 B.C., the Phoenicians, a people who also lived in the Middle East, created a less clumsy writing system. Instead of combining pictures to make sounds, they developed an alphabet. Each letter in the alphabet stood for a sound. To form words, several sounds were blended together. The alphabet that we use today comes from the original Phoenician alphabet.

1. How is ancient Egyptian writing different from the way we write?
2. What is the importance of the Rosetta Stone?

Oral Fluency Record Sheet

Name ________________________________ Date ______________

Oral Reading Accuracy: ________%

Oral Reading Fluency Score: ____________ words correct per minute

Prosody Rubric: (Circle Score) 1 2 3 4

Comprehension Question Responses

#1 ________________________________

#2 ________________________________

Egyptian Writing

	Egyptian picture writing, or hieroglyphics, began almost
7	5,000 years ago. At first, the Egyptians just drew pictures to stand
19	for objects. For example, the sun was a circle with a dot in it. A
34	house was a small rectangle. Over time, it became too difficult to
46	come up with a new picture for each word. So the Egyptians began
59	to combine words to make sounds. For example, the Egyptian
69	word for "go out" sounds like the words for "house" and "sun."
81	Writers just combined these two pictures when they needed to write
92	the word that means "go out."
98	Over the centuries, the ability to understand Egyptian
106	writing was lost. Experts puzzled over Egyptian texts without any
116	idea of what they meant. Then, in 1799, an officer in the French
129	army found the Rosetta Stone in Egypt. The strange black stone
140	had three sections of writing carved into it. The first section was a
153	story in Greek. The other two sections were translations of the
164	same story into Egyptian picture writing. Using these translations,
173	experts quickly decoded the Rosetta Stone. Using what they
182	deciphered, they soon solved the puzzle of Egyptian hieroglyphics.
191	Picture writing was used for thousands of years. But by
201	1000 B.C., the Phoenicians, a people who also lived in the Middle
213	East, created a less clumsy writing system. Instead of combining
223	pictures to make sounds, they developed an alphabet. Each letter in
234	the alphabet stood for a sound. To form words, several sounds
245	were blended together. The alphabet that we use today comes from
256	the original Phoenician alphabet. **260**

Number of words read: __________ **Number of errors made: __________**

from The Talking Skull

by Donna L. Washington

Once a man was walking down the road toward his village. He was not paying attention to anything around him. This man considered himself a scholar of life. He was always deep in thought. He liked to think about important things. He did not put his mind to ordinary problems. If it wasn't impossible, or at least very complicated, he didn't care about it at all.

This man spent all day looking out over the ocean, and he only noticed things he thought were useful. He didn't notice the beauty of the ocean. The only things he considered were sharks and shipwrecks. He didn't notice the clear blue sky. He was thinking about all the storms that must have been churning far away. He did not notice the wonderful songs of the birds. He only thought about how many of their nests had been robbed. He didn't notice the playful animals swinging through the branches or rustling in the grass. He only wondered whether or not the great cats were on the prowl. That was the kind of man he was.

Oral Fluency Record Sheet

Name ______________________________ Date ______________

Oral Reading Accuracy: __________%
Oral Reading Fluency Score: ______________ **words correct per minute**
Prosody Rubric: (Circle Score) 1 2 3 4
Comprehension Question Responses
#1 ______________________________
#2 ______________________________

The Talking Skull

	Once a man was walking down the road
8	toward his village. He was not paying attention
16	to anything around him. This man considered
23	himself a scholar of life. He was always deep
32	in thought. He liked to think about important
40	things. He did not put his mind to ordinary
49	problems. If it wasn't impossible, or at least
57	very complicated, he didn't care about it at all.
66	This man spent all day looking out over the
75	ocean, and he only noticed things he thought
83	were useful. He didn't notice the beauty of
91	the ocean. The only things he considered
98	were sharks and shipwrecks. He didn't notice
105	the clear blue sky. He was thinking about all
114	the storms that must have been churning far
122	away. He did not notice the wonderful songs
130	of the birds. He only thought about how many
139	of their nests had been robbed. He didn't
147	notice the playful animals swinging through
153	the branches or rustling in the grass. He only
162	wondered whether or not the great cats were on
171	the prowl. That was the kind of man he was. **181**

Number of words read: __________ **Number of errors made:** __________

from The Circuit

by Francisco Jimenez

As we drove home Papa did not say a word. With both hands on the wheel, he stared at the dirt road. My older brother, Roberto, was also silent. He leaned his head back and closed his eyes. Once in a while he cleared from his throat the dust that blew in from outside.

Yes, it was that time of year. When I opened the front door to the shack, I stopped. Everything we owned was neatly packed in cardboard boxes. Suddenly I felt even more the weight of hours, days, weeks, and months of work. I sat down on a box. The thought of having to move to Fresno and knowing what was in store for me there brought tears to my eyes.

That night I could not sleep. I lay in bed thinking about how much I hated this move.

A little before five o'clock in the morning, Papa woke everyone up.

Oral Fluency Record Sheet

Name ______________________________ Date ______________

Oral Reading Accuracy: __________%
Oral Reading Fluency Score: ______________ **words correct per minute**
Prosody Rubric: (Circle Score) 1 2 3 4
Comprehension Question Responses
#1 ______________________________
#2 ______________________________

The Circuit

	As we drove home Papa did not say a
9	word. With both hands on the wheel, he
17	stared at the dirt road. My older brother,
25	Roberto, was also silent. He leaned his
32	head back and closed his eyes. Once in a
41	while he cleared from his throat the dust
49	that blew in from outside.
54	Yes, it was that time of year. When I
63	opened the front door to the shack, I
71	stopped. Everything we owned was neatly
77	packed in cardboard boxes. Suddenly I felt
84	even more the weight of hours, days,
91	weeks, and months of work. I sat down on
100	a box. The thought of having to move to
109	Fresno and knowing what was in store for
117	me there brought tears to my eyes.
124	That night I could not sleep. I lay in
133	bed thinking about how much I hated
140	this move.
142	A little before five o'clock in the
149	morning, Papa woke everyone up. 154

Number of words read: __________ **Number of errors made:** __________

from The Real Magic of Harry Potter

by Nancy Gibbs

It's probably no surprise to Rowling's fans that many children buy the books with their own money. Or that they wear out flashlight batteries reading the books after lights-out. And, no surprise here, even readers who dislike thick books have read Harry Potter not once or twice but a dozen times. For many fans, the books are far better than watching TV or staring at a computer screen.

When the fifth book in the series, *Harry Potter and the Order of the Phoenix*, was published in June 2003, it created a lot of excitement. There were Potter parties complete with owls, cloaks, and butterbeer. Kids wore their Potter pajamas. They even wanted to sleep in a "cupboard under the stairs," as Harry is forced to do by his creepy adopted family on Privet Drive. Some families ordered two or three books so that everyone could read the book at the same time. At close to 900 pages, *Harry Potter and the Order of the Phoenix* is the longest children's book there is. It was the best seller online only two hours after it was possible for computer users to order copies of it.

Oral Fluency Record Sheet

Name ______________________________ Date ______________

Oral Reading Accuracy: __________%
Oral Reading Fluency Score: ____________ **words correct per minute**
Prosody Rubric: (Circle Score) 1 2 3 4
Comprehension Question Responses
#1 ______________________________
#2 ______________________________

The Real Magic of Harry Potter

	It's probably no surprise to Rowling's fans
7	that many children buy the books with their
15	own money. Or that they wear out flashlight
23	batteries reading the books after lights-out.
30	And, no surprise here, even readers who dislike
38	thick books have read Harry Potter not once
46	or twice but a dozen times. For many fans, the
56	books are far better than watching TV or staring
65	at a computer screen.
69	When the fifth book in the series, *Harry*
77	*Potter and the Order of the Phoenix*, was
85	published in June 2003, it created a lot of
94	excitement. There were Potter parties complete
100	with owls, cloaks, and butterbeer. Kids wore
107	their Potter pajamas. They even wanted to sleep
115	in a "cupboard under the stairs," as Harry is
124	forced to do by his creepy adopted family on
133	Privet Drive. Some families ordered two or
140	three books so that everyone could read the
148	book at the same time. At close to 900 pages,
158	*Harry Potter and the Order of the Phoenix* is
167	the longest children's book there is. It was
175	the best seller online only two hours after it was
185	possible for computer users to order copies of it. 194

Number of words read: __________ **Number of errors made:** __________

from Harriet Tubman: Conductor on the Underground Railroad

by Ann Petry

Harriet Tubman could have told them that there was more involved in this matter of running off slaves than signaling the would-be runaways by imitating the call of a whippoorwill, or a hoot owl, far more involved than a matter of waiting for a clear night when the North Star was visible.

In December, 1851, when she started out with the band of fugitives that she planned to take to Canada, she had been in the vicinity of the plantation for days, planning the trip, carefully selecting the slaves that she would take with her. She had announced her arrival in the quarter by singing the forbidden spiritual—"Go Down, Moses, 'way down to Egypt Land"—singing it softly outside the door of a slave cabin, late at night. The husky voice was beautiful even when it was barely more than a murmur borne on the wind.

Once she made her presence known, word of her coming spread from cabin to cabin. The slaves whispered to each other, ear to mouth, mouth to ear, "Moses is here." "Moses has come." "Get ready. Moses is back again."

Oral Fluency Record Sheet

Name ______________________________ Date ______________

Oral Reading Accuracy: ________%

Oral Reading Fluency Score: ______________ **words correct per minute**

Prosody Rubric: (Circle Score) 1 2 3 4

Comprehension Question Responses

#1 ______________________________

#2 ______________________________

Harriet Tubman: Conductor on the Underground Railroad

	Harriet Tubman could have told them that there
8	was more involved in this matter of running off
17	slaves than signaling the would-be runaways by
25	imitating the call of a whippoorwill, or a hoot owl,
35	far more involved than a matter of waiting for a
45	clear night when the North Star was visible.
53	In December, 1851, when she started out with
61	the band of fugitives that she planned to take to
71	Canada, she had been in the vicinity of the
80	plantation for days, planning the trip, carefully
87	selecting the slaves that she would take with her.
96	She had announced her arrival in the quarter by
105	singing the forbidden spiritual—"Go Down, Moses,
112	'way down to Egypt Land"—singing it softly
120	outside the door of a slave cabin, late at night. The
131	husky voice was beautiful even when it was barely
140	more than a murmur borne on the wind.
148	Once she made her presence known, word of her
157	coming spread from cabin to cabin. The slaves
165	whispered to each other, ear to mouth, mouth to ear,
175	"Moses is here." "Moses has come." "Get ready.
183	Moses is back again." **187**

Number of words read: __________ **Number of errors made:** __________

from The Monsters Are Due on Maple Street

by Rod Serling

NARRATOR'S VOICE. Maple Street. Six-forty-four p.m. on a late September evening. [A pause.] Maple Street in the last calm and reflective moment . . . before the monsters came!

[The camera slowly pans across the porches again. We see a man screwing a light bulb on a front porch, then getting down off the stool to flick the switch and finding that nothing happens. Another man is working on an electric power mower. He plugs in the plug, flicks on the switch of the power mower, off and on, with nothing happening. Through the window of a front porch, we see a woman pushing her finger back and forth on the dial hook. Her voice is indistinct and distant, but intelligible and repetitive.]

WOMAN. Operator, operator, something's wrong on the phone, operator!

[MRS. BRAND comes out on the porch and calls to STEVE.]

MRS. BRAND. [Calling.] Steve, the power's off. I had the soup on the stove and the stove just stopped working.

WOMAN. Same thing over here. I can't get anybody on the phone either. The phone seems to be dead.

[We look down on the street as we hear the voices creep up from below, small, mildly disturbed voices highlighting these kinds of phrases:]

VOICES.

Electricity's off.

Phone won't work.

Can't get a thing on the radio.

My power mower won't move, won't work at all.

Radio's gone dead!

Oral Fluency Record Sheet

Name ______________________________ Date ______________

Oral Reading Accuracy: __________%
Oral Reading Fluency Score: ______________ **words correct per minute**
Prosody Rubric: (Circle Score) 1 2 3 4
Comprehension Question Responses
#1 ____
#2 ____

The Monsters Are Due on Maple Street

	NARRATOR'S VOICE. Maple Street. Six-forty-four p.m. on
9	a late September evening. [A pause.] Maple Street in the last
20	calm and reflective moment . . . before the monsters came!
28	[The camera slowly pans across the porches again. We
37	see a man screwing a light bulb on a front porch, then
49	getting down off the stool to flick the switch and finding
60	that nothing happens. Another man is working on an
69	electric power mower. He plugs in the plug, flicks on
79	the switch of the power mower, off and on, with nothing
90	happening. Through the window of a front porch, we see
100	a woman pushing her finger back and forth on the dial
111	hook. Her voice is indistinct and distant, but intelligible
120	and repetitive.]
122	**WOMAN.** Operator, operator, something's wrong on the
129	phone, operator!
131	[MRS. BRAND comes out on the porch and calls to STEVE.]
142	**MRS. BRAND.** [Calling.] Steve, the power's off. I had the
152	soup on the stove and the stove just stopped working.
162	**WOMAN.** Same thing over here. I can't get anybody on the
173	phone either. The phone seems to be dead.
181	[We look down on the street as we hear the voices creep
193	up from below, small, mildly disturbed voices highlighting
201	these kinds of phrases:]
205	**VOICES.**
206	Electricity's off.
208	Phone won't work.
211	Can't get a thing on the radio.
218	My power mower won't move, won't work at all.
227	Radio's gone dead! **230**

Number of words read: __________ **Number of errors made:** __________

from A Child's Christmas in Wales

by Dylan Thomas

It was on the afternoon of the day of Christmas Eve, and I was in Mrs. Prothero's garden, waiting for cats, with her son Jim. It was snowing. It was always snowing at Christmas. December, in my memory, is white as Lapland, though there were no reindeers. But there were cats. Patient, cold, and callous, our hands wrapped in socks, we waited to snowball the cats. Sleek and long as jaguars and horrible-whiskered, spitting and snarling, they would slink and sidle over the white back-garden walls, and the lynx-eyed hunters, Jim and I, fur-capped and moccasined trappers from Hudson Bay, off Mumbles Road, would hurl our deadly snowballs at the green of their eyes.

The wise cats never appeared. We were so still, Eskimo-footed arctic marksmen in the muffling silence of the eternal snows—eternal, ever since Wednesday—that we never heard Mrs. Prothero's first cry from her igloo at the bottom of the garden. Or, if we heard it at all, it was, to us, like the far-off challenge of our enemy and prey, the neighbour's polar cat. But soon the voice grew louder. "Fire!" cried Mrs. Prothero, and she beat the dinner-gong.

And we ran down the garden, with the snowballs in our arms, toward the house; and smoke, indeed, was pouring out of the dining-room, and the gong was bombilating, and Mrs. Prothero was announcing ruin like a town crier in Pompeii. This was better than all the cats in Wales standing on the wall in a row. We bounded into the house, laden with snowballs, and stopped at the open door of the smoke-filled room.

Something was burning all right; perhaps it was Mr. Prothero, who always slept there after midday dinner with a newspaper over his face. But he was standing in the middle of the room, saying, "A fine Christmas!" and smacking at the smoke with a slipper. "Call the fire brigade," cried Mrs. Prothero as she beat the gong.

"They won't be there," said Mr. Prothero, "it's Christmas."

There was no fire to be seen, only clouds of smoke and Mr. Prothero standing in the middle of them, waving his slipper as though he were conducting.

"Do something," he said.

And we threw all our snowballs into the smoke—I think we missed Mr. Prothero—and ran out of the house to the telephone box.

"Let's call the police as well," Jim said.

"And the ambulance."

"And Ernie Jenkins, he likes fires."

Oral Fluency Record Sheet

Name ______________________________ Date ______________

Oral Reading Accuracy: ________%

Oral Reading Fluency Score: ____________ **words correct per minute**

Prosody Rubric: (Circle Score) 1 2 3 4

Comprehension Question Responses

#1 ______________________________

#2 ______________________________

A Child's Christmas in Wales

	It was on the afternoon of the day of Christmas Eve,
11	and I was in Mrs. Prothero's garden, waiting for cats, with
22	her son Jim. It was snowing. It was always snowing at
33	Christmas. December, in my memory, is white as Lapland,
42	though there were no reindeers. But there were cats. Patient,
52	cold, and callous, our hands wrapped in socks, we waited
62	to snowball the cats. Sleek and long as jaguars and horrible-
73	whiskered, spitting and snarling, they would slink and
81	sidle over the white back-garden walls, and the lynx-eyed
92	hunters, Jim and I, fur-capped and moccasined trappers
101	from Hudson Bay, off Mumbles Road, would hurl our
110	deadly snowballs at the green of their eyes.
118	The wise cats never appeared. We were so still, Eskimo-
128	footed arctic marksmen in the muffling silence of the eternal
138	snows—eternal, ever since Wednesday—that we never
146	heard Mrs. Prothero's first cry from her igloo at the bottom
157	of the garden. Or, if we heard it at all, it was, to us, like the
173	far-off challenge of our enemy and prey, the neighbour's
183	polar cat. But soon the voice grew louder. "Fire!" cried Mrs.
194	Prothero, and she beat the dinner-gong.
201	And we ran down the garden, with the snowballs in our
212	arms, toward the house; and smoke, indeed, was pouring
221	out of the dining-room, and the gong was bombilating,
231	and Mrs. Prothero was announcing ruin like a town crier in
242	Pompeii. This was better than all the cats in Wales standing
253	on the wall in a row. We bounded into the house, laden with
266	snowballs, and stopped at the open door of the smoke-
276	filled room.

278 Something was burning all right; perhaps it was Mr.
287 Prothero, who always slept there after midday dinner with a
297 newspaper over his face. But he was standing in the middle
308 of the room, saying, "A fine Christmas!" and smacking at
318 the smoke with a slipper. "Call the fire brigade," cried Mrs.
329 Prothero as she beat the gong.
335 "They won't be there," said Mr. Prothero,
342 "it's Christmas."
344 There was no fire to be seen, only clouds of smoke and
356 Mr. Prothero standing in the middle of them, waving his
366 slipper as though he were conducting.
372 "Do something," he said.
376 And we threw all our snowballs into the smoke—I think
387 we missed Mr. Prothero—and ran out of the house to the
399 telephone box.
401 "Let's call the police as well," Jim said.
409 "And the ambulance."
412 "And Ernie Jenkins, he likes fires." **418**

Number of words read: ________ **Number of errors made:** ________

from Charles

by Shirley Jackson

The day my son Laurie started kindergarten he renounced corduroy overalls with bibs and began wearing blue jeans with a belt; I watched him go off the first morning with the older girl next door, seeing clearly that an era of my life was ended, my sweet-voiced nursery-school tot replaced by a long-trousered, swaggering character who forgot to stop at the corner and wave good-bye to me.

He came home the same way, the front door slamming open, his cap on the floor, and the voice suddenly become raucous shouting, "Isn't anybody *here*?"

At lunch he spoke insolently to his father, spilled his baby sister's milk, and remarked that his teacher said we were not to take the name of the Lord in vain.

"How was school today?" I asked, elaborately casual.

"All right," he said.

"Did you learn anything?" his father asked.

Laurie regarded his father coldly. "I didn't learn nothing," he said.

Oral Fluency Record Sheet

Name ______________________________ Date ______________

Oral Reading Accuracy: __________%

Oral Reading Fluency Score: ______________ **words correct per minute**

Prosody Rubric: (Circle Score) 1 2 3 4

Comprehension Question Responses

#1 ______________________________

#2 ______________________________

Charles

	The day my son Laurie started kindergarten
7	he renounced corduroy overalls with bibs
13	and began wearing blue jeans with a belt;
21	I watched him go off the first morning with
30	the older girl next door, seeing clearly that an
39	era of my life was ended, my sweet-voiced
48	nursery-school tot replaced by a
54	long-trousered, swaggering character who
59	forgot to stop at the corner and wave
67	good-bye to me.
71	He came home the same way, the front
79	door slamming open, his cap on the floor,
87	and the voice suddenly become raucous
93	shouting, "Isn't anybody *here*?"
97	At lunch he spoke insolently to his
104	father, spilled his baby sister's milk, and
111	remarked that his teacher said we were not
119	to take the name of the Lord in vain.
128	"How was school today?" I asked,
134	elaborately casual.
136	"All right," he said.
140	"Did you learn anything?" his
145	father asked.
147	Laurie regarded his father coldly. "I
153	didn't learn nothing," he said. **158**

Number of words read: __________ **Number of errors made:** __________

from Priscilla and the Wimps

by Richard Peck

Listen, there was a time when you couldn't even go to the *rest room* around this school without a pass. And I'm not talking about those little pink tickets made out by some teacher. I'm talking about a pass that could cost anywhere up to a buck, sold by Monk Klutter.

Not that Mighty Monk ever touched money, not in public. The gang he ran, which ran the school for him, was his collection agency. They were Klutter's Kobras, spelled out in nailheads on six well-known black plastic windbreakers.

Monk's threads were more . . . subtle. A pile-lined suede battle jacket with lizard-skin flaps over tailored jeans and a pair of ostrich-skin boots, brassed-toed and suitable for kicking people around. One of his Kobras did nothing all day but walk a half step behind Monk, carrying a fitted bag with Monk's gym shoes, a roll of restroom passes, a cashbox, and a switchblade that Monk gave himself manicures with at lunch over at the Kobras' table.

Oral Fluency Record Sheet

Name ______________________________ Date ______________

Oral Reading Accuracy: __________%
Oral Reading Fluency Score: ______________ **words correct per minute**
Prosody Rubric: (Circle Score) 1 2 3 4
Comprehension Question Responses
#1 ______________________________
#2 ______________________________

Priscilla and the Wimps

	Listen, there was a time when you
7	couldn't even go to the *rest room* around
15	this school without a pass. And I'm not
23	talking about those little pink tickets made
30	out by some teacher. I'm talking about a
38	pass that could cost anywhere up to a buck,
47	sold by Monk Klutter.
51	Not that Mighty Monk ever touched
57	money, not in public. The gang he ran,
65	which ran the school for him, was his
73	collection agency. They were Klutter's
78	Kobras, spelled out in nailheads on
84	six well-known black plastic windbreakers.
90	Monk's threads were more . . . subtle.
95	A pile-lined suede battle jacket with
102	lizard-skin flaps over tailored jeans and a
110	pair of ostrich-skin boots, brassed-toed and
118	suitable for kicking people around. One of
125	his Kobras did nothing all day but walk a
134	half step behind Monk, carrying a fitted bag
142	with Monk's gym shoes, a roll of restroom
150	passes, a cashbox, and a switchblade that
157	Monk gave himself manicures with at lunch
164	over at the Kobras' table. **169**

Number of words read: __________ **Number of errors made:** __________

from Aunt Millicent

by Mary Steele

Grandma pondered a moment. "Now that you mention it, she did. She did indeed. I thought we'd have to chain her up sometime! We lived near the edge of town, you'll remember, and Millie would look out towards the paddocks and hills and say that she wanted to know what was over the horizon, or where the birds were flying to, or where the clouds came from behind the hills. We never knew where she'd be off to next—but she certainly ended up in the right job! I'm so glad she became an explorer. If I were a bit younger and had better feet, I might even go and join her. It would be most interesting to see the Cameroons. It's full of monkeys, I believe."

"Was Aunt Millicent good at geography at school?" Nerissa remembered to ask.

"Let me think—yes, she must have been because one year she won a prize for it, and the prize was a book called *Lives of the Great Explorers.*"

Oral Fluency Record Sheet

Name ______________________________ Date ______________

Oral Reading Accuracy: __________%
Oral Reading Fluency Score: ______________ **words correct per minute**
Prosody Rubric: (Circle Score) 1 2 3 4
Comprehension Question Responses
#1 ______________________________
#2 ______________________________

Aunt Millicent

	Grandma pondered a moment. "Now
5	that you mention it, she did. She did indeed.
14	I thought we'd have to chain her up sometime!
23	We lived near the edge of town, you'll
31	remember, and Millie would look out towards
38	the paddocks and hills and say that she wanted
47	to know what was over the horizon, or where
56	the birds were flying to, or where the clouds
65	came from behind the hills. We never knew
73	where she'd be off to next—but she certainly
82	ended up in the right job! I'm so glad she
92	became an explorer. If I were a bit younger
101	and had better feet, I might even go and join
111	her. It would be most interesting to see the
120	Cameroons. It's full of monkeys, I believe."
127	"Was Aunt Millicent good at geography at
134	school?" Nerissa remembered to ask.
139	"Let me think—yes, she must have been
147	because one year she won a prize for it, and
157	the prize was a book called *Lives of the*
166	*Great Explorers.*" **168**

Number of words read: __________ **Number of errors made:** __________

from What Makes Teens Tick?

by Claudia Wallis

Before birth, nerve cells in the brain undergo a phase in which they multiply and grow rapidly. Then the brain gets rid of cells that aren't needed. Giedd's studies show that brain cells undergo a second phase of change that starts in childhood and lasts until the early twenties. Unlike the earlier phase, which changes the number of nerve cells, the second one changes the number of connections between the nerve cells.

When a child is between 6 and 12 years old, nerve cells become bushier. Each nerve cell branches out to other nerve cells. These branches carry signals between the cells. This process peaks when girls are about 11 and boys are about 12½. Then some of the branches are slowly thinned out over several years.

At the same time, a fatty layer covers the branches of the nerve cells that remain. With each passing year, the fatty coverings thicken, much like tree rings. During this time, a person's brain has fewer fast connections. It's a trade-off. The brain becomes more efficient but is probably losing its potential for learning and its ability to recover from trauma.

Oral Fluency Record Sheet

Name ______________________________ Date ______________

Oral Reading Accuracy: __________%

Oral Reading Fluency Score: ______________ words correct per minute

Prosody Rubric: (Circle Score) 1 2 3 4

Comprehension Question Responses

#1 ______________________________

#2 ______________________________

What Makes Teens Tick?

	Before birth, nerve cells in the brain
7	undergo a phase in which they multiply and
15	grow rapidly. Then the brain gets rid of cells
24	that aren't needed. Giedd's studies show that
31	brain cells undergo a second phase of change
39	that starts in childhood and lasts until the
47	early twenties. Unlike the earlier phase, which
54	changes the number of nerve cells, the second
62	one changes the number of connections between
69	the nerve cells.
72	When a child is between 6 and 12 years
81	old, nerve cells become bushier. Each nerve
88	cell branches out to other nerve cells. These
96	branches carry signals between the cells. This
103	process peaks when girls are about 11 and boys
112	are about 12½. Then some of the branches are
121	slowly thinned out over several years.
127	At the same time, a fatty layer covers the
136	branches of the nerve cells that remain. With
144	each passing year, the fatty coverings thicken,
151	much like tree rings. During this time, a
159	person's brain has fewer fast connections. It's a
167	trade-off. The brain becomes more efficient but
175	is probably losing its potential for learning and
183	its ability to recover from trauma. **189**

Number of words read: __________ **Number of errors made:** __________

Centuries of Whaling

When Vikings roamed the Atlantic Ocean long ago, one of the greatest prizes they sought were whales. Way back in the 1100s, the struggle between whale and sailor was a fairly even one, but over time, whaling methods grew more and more advanced. By the middle 1800s, whaling had become a big business.

Norwegian whalers, the modern relatives of the Vikings, were among the leaders in whaling technology. In 1863, a Norwegian sea captain created a new type of whaling ship. The 82-foot-long boat was sleek and swift, fast enough to catch up with even the fastest swimming whale. It also had bomb harpoons. These harpoons were tipped with bombs that would explode inside the whale. They caused death much sooner than ordinary harpoons. Suddenly, the seas were even more dangerous than ever for whales.

By the late 1800s, many whale species were endangered. The numbers of both the right whale and the bowhead whale dropped sharply. Because these whales were slower than the new boats, they were easy to kill. Sadly, millions of whales were slaughtered before a ban on whaling was agreed upon in 1982. Since then, whaling has been prohibited and successfully suppressed.

But almost all kinds of whales still suffer because of the extensive whaling in the past. Some whales, like the gray whale, have recovered quite nicely. Their numbers continue to grow. Others, like the northern right whale, continue to be in danger of extinction. At the present time, fewer than 400 northern right whales exist in the whole world. Only time will tell if whales can survive the effects of centuries of whaling.

1. What is the passage mostly about?
2. What finally stopped widespread whaling?

Oral Fluency Record Sheet

Name ______________________ Date __________

Oral Reading Accuracy: ________%

Oral Reading Fluency Score: __________ words correct per minute

Prosody Rubric: (Circle Score) 1 2 3 4

Comprehension Question Responses

#1 ______________________

#2 ______________________

Centuries of Whaling

When Vikings roamed the Atlantic Ocean long ago, one
9 of the greatest prizes they sought were whales. Way back in
20 the 1100s, the struggle between whale and sailor was a fairly
31 even one, but over time, whaling methods grew more and
41 more advanced. By the middle 1800s, whaling had become a
51 big business.

53 Norwegian whalers, the modern relatives of the Vikings,
61 were among the leaders in whaling technology. In 1863, a
71 Norwegian sea captain created a new type of whaling ship. The
82 82-foot-long boat was sleek and swift, fast enough to catch up
95 with even the fastest swimming whale. It also had bomb harpoons.
106 These harpoons were tipped with bombs that would explode inside
116 the whale. They caused death much sooner than ordinary
125 harpoons. Suddenly, the seas were even more dangerous than
134 ever for whales.

137 By the late 1800s, many whale species were endangered.
146 The numbers of both the right whale and the bowhead whale
157 dropped sharply. Because these whales were slower than the new
167 boats, they were easy to kill. Sadly, millions of whales were
178 slaughtered before a ban on whaling was agreed upon in 1982.
189 Since then, whaling has been prohibited and successfully
197 suppressed.

198 But almost all kinds of whales still suffer because of the
209 extensive whaling in the past. Some whales, like the gray whale,
220 have recovered quite nicely. Their numbers continue to grow.
229 Others, like the northern right whale, continue to be in danger of
241 extinction. At the present time, fewer than 400 northern right
251 whales exist in the whole world. Only time will tell if whales can
264 survive the effects of centuries of whaling. **271**

Number of words read: __________ Number of errors made: __________

from I Have a Dream

by Martin Luther King, Jr.

It is obvious today that America has defaulted on this promissory note in so far as her citizens of color are concerned. Instead of honoring the sacred obligation, America has given the Negro people a bad check, a check which has come back marked "insufficient funds." We refuse to believe that there are insufficient funds in the great vaults of opportunity of this nation. And so we've come to cash this check, a check that will give us upon demand the riches of freedom and the security of justice.

We have also come to this hallowed spot to remind America of the fierce urgency of now. This is no time to engage in the luxury of cooling off or take the tranquilizing drug of gradualism. Now is the time to make real the promises of democracy; now is the time to rise from the dark and desolate valley of segregation to the sunlit path of racial justice; now is the time to lift our nation from the quicksands of racial injustice to the solid rock of brotherhood; now is the time to make justice a reality for all God's children.

Oral Fluency Record Sheet

Name ______________________ Date __________

Oral Reading Accuracy: ________%
Oral Reading Fluency Score: ____________ **words correct per minute**
Prosody Rubric: (Circle Score) 1 2 3 4
Comprehension Question Responses
#1 ______________________
#2 ______________________

I Have a Dream

	It is obvious today that America has
7	defaulted on this promissory note in so far as
16	her citizens of color are concerned. Instead of
24	honoring the sacred obligation, America has
30	given the Negro people a bad check, a check
39	which has come back marked "insufficient
45	funds." We refuse to believe that there are
53	insufficient funds in the great vaults of
60	opportunity of this nation. And so we've come
68	to cash this check, a check that will give us
78	upon demand the riches of freedom and the
86	security of justice.
89	We have also come to this hallowed spot
97	to remind America of the fierce urgency of
105	now. This is no time to engage in the luxury
115	of cooling off or take the tranquilizing drug
123	of gradualism. Now is the time to make real
132	the promises of democracy; now is the time
140	to rise from the dark and desolate valley of
149	segregation to the sunlit path of racial justice;
157	now is the time to lift our nation from the
167	quicksands of racial injustice to the solid rock of
176	brotherhood; now is the time to make justice a
185	reality for all God's children. **190**

Number of words read: ________ **Number of errors made:** ________

2005 National Fluency Norms

Jan Hasbrouck and Gerald Tindal completed an extensive study of oral reading fluency in 2004. The results of their study are published in a technical report entitled, "Oral Reading Fluency: 90 Years of Measurement," which is available on the University of Oregon's Web site, **brt.uoregon.edu/tech_reports.htm**.

This table shows the oral reading fluency rates of students in Grades 1 through 8 as determined by Hasbrouck and Tindal's data.

You can use the information in this table to draw conclusions and make decisions about the oral reading fluency of your students. **Students scoring below the 50th percentile using the average score of two unpracticed readings from grade-level materials need a fluency-building program.** In addition, teachers can use the table to set the long-term fluency goals for their struggling readers.

Average weekly improvement is the average words per week growth you can expect from a student. It was calculated by subtracting the fall score from the spring score and dividing the difference by 32, the typical number of weeks between the fall and spring assessments. For Grade 1, since there is no fall assessment, the average weekly improvement was calculated by subtracting the winter score from the spring score and dividing the difference by 16, the typical number of weeks between the winter and spring assessments.

Grade	Percentile	Fall WCPM*	Winter WCPM*	Spring WCPM*	Avg. Weekly Improvement**
1	90		81	111	1.9
	75		47	82	2.2
	50		23	53	1.9
	25		12	28	1.0
	10		6	15	0.6
2	90	106	125	142	1.1
	75	79	100	117	1.2
	50	51	72	89	1.2
	25	25	42	61	1.1
	10	11	18	31	0.6

*WCPM = Words Correct Per Minute

Oral Reading Fluency Data

Grade	Percentile	Fall WCPM*	Winter WCPM*	Spring WCPM*	Avg. Weekly Improvement**
3	90	128	146	162	1.1
	75	99	120	137	1.2
	50	71	92	107	1.1
	25	44	62	78	1.1
	10	21	36	48	0.8
4	90	145	166	180	1.1
	75	119	139	152	1.0
	50	94	112	123	0.9
	25	68	87	98	0.9
	10	45	61	72	0.8
5	90	166	182	194	0.9
	75	139	156	168	0.9
	50	110	127	139	0.9
	25	85	99	109	0.8
	10	61	74	83	0.7
6	90	177	195	204	0.8
	75	153	167	177	0.8
	50	127	140	150	0.7
	25	98	111	122	0.8
	10	68	82	93	0.8
7	90	180	192	202	0.7
	75	156	165	177	0.7
	50	128	136	150	0.7
	25	102	109	123	0.7
	10	79	88	98	0.6
8	90	185	199	199	0.4
	75	161	173	177	0.5
	50	133	146	151	0.6
	25	106	115	124	0.6
	10	77	84	97	0.6

**Average words per week growth

K–8 Diagnostic Assessment

Spelling

"Words Their Way" Qualitative Spelling Inventory

Skill Assessed
Spelling

Grade Level
- Primary K–3
- Elementary K–6
- Upper Level, 6–8
- English

Group/individual

Approximate Testing Time
10–15 Minutes

▶ **WHAT** The *"Words Their Way" Qualitative Spelling Inventory* consists of three inventories: one for primary students in grades K–3, one for elementary students in grades 1–6, and one for upper level students in grades 4–8 and above. The inventories are administered in the same way as a standard spelling test. The focus of this inventory, in contrast to the typical spelling test, is to examine the types of errors made by students as well as to take note of correctly spelled words. Through this examination, the student's skills can be classified as falling into a particular developmental stage of spelling. Bear and his co-authors identify the five developmental spelling stages listed below. A Grouping example of spelling at each stage is also shown.

Materials
Pencil or pen
Lined paper
Source: *Words Their Way: Word Study for Phonics, Vocabulary & Spelling Instruction* by Donald Bear, Marcia Invernizzi, Shane Templeton, and Francine Johnston

Spelling Stages	
Stage 1. Preliterate	Marks on the page
Stage 2. Letter Name	bd for *bed*
Stage 3. Within Word Pattern	*traen* for *train*
Stage 4. Syllable Juncture	*confedent* for *confident*
Stage 5. Derivational Constancy	*emphasize* for *emphasize* (spelled correctly)

HOW General Directions for Administering the Inventories

Students should not study the words in advance of testing. Assure students that they will not be graded on this activity, and that they will be helping you plan for their needs. Following is a possible introduction to the assessment.

I am going to ask you to spell some words. Spell them the best you can. Some of the words may be easy to spell; some may be difficult. When you do not know how to spell a word, spell it the best you can.

Ask students to number their paper (or prepare a numbered paper for kindergarten or early first grade). Call each word aloud and repeat it. Say each word naturally, with-out emphasizing phonemes or syllables. Use it in a sentence, if necessary, to be sure students know the exact word. Sample sentences are provided along with the words. After administering the inventory, use a Feature Guide, Class Composite Form, and, if desired, a Spelling-by-Stage Classroom Organization Chart to complete your assessment.

Scoring the Inventory Using the Feature Guides

1. Make a copy of the appropriate Feature Guide (PSI pp. 7–8, ESI pp. 12–13, USI pp. 18–19) for each student. Draw a line under the last word called if you called fewer than the total number and adjust the possible total points at the bottom of each feature column.
2. Score the words by checking off the features spelled correctly that are listed in the cells to the left of each word. For example, if a student spells *bed* as *bad*, he gets a check in the initial *b* cell and the final *d* cell, but not for the short vowel. Write in the vowel used (*a*, in this case), but do not give any points for it. If a student spells *train* as *trane*, she gets a check in the initial *tr* cell and the final *n* cell, but not for the long vowel pattern. Write in the vowel pattern used (*a-e* in this case), but do not give any points for it. Put a check in the "Correct" column if the word is spelled correctly. Do not count reversed letters as errors but note them in the cells. If unnecessary letters are added, give the speller credit for what is correct (e.g., if *bed* is spelled *bede*, the student still gets credit for representing the short vowel), but do not check "Correct" spelling.
3. Add the number of checks under each feature and across each word, double-checking the total score recorded in the last cell. Modify the ratios in the last row depending on the number of words called aloud.

Interpreting the Results of the Spelling Inventory

1. Look down each feature column to determine instructional needs. Students who miss only one (or two, if the features sample 8 to 10 words) can go on to other features. Students who miss two or three need some review work; students who miss more than three need careful instruction on this feature. If a student did not get any points for a feature, earlier features need to be studied first.
2. To determine a stage of development, note where students first make two or more errors under the stages listed in the shaded box at the top of the Feature Guide. Circle this stage.

Using the Class Composite and Spelling by Stage Form

1. Staple each Feature Guide to the student's spelling paper and arrange the papers in rank order from highest total points to lowest total points.
2. List students' names in this rank order in the left column of the appropriate Classroom Composite (PSI pp. 9–10, ESI pp. 14–15, USI pp. 20–21) and transfer each student's feature scores from the bottom row of the individual Feature Guides to the Classroom Composite. If you do not call out the total list, adjust the totals on the bottom row of the Classroom Composite.
3. Highlight cells where students make two or more errors on a particular feature to get a sense of your groups' needs and to form groups for instruction.
4. Many teachers find it easier to form groups using the Spelling-by-Stage Classroom Organization Chart. List each student under the appropriate spelling stage (the stage circled on the Feature Guide) and determine instructional groups.

Primary Spelling Inventory (PSI)

The Primary Spelling Inventory (PSI) is used in kindergarten through third grade. The 26 words are ordered by difficulty to sample features of the letter name-alphabetic to within word pattern stages. Call out enough words so that you have at least five or six misspelled words to analyze. For kindergarten or other emergent readers, you may only need to call out the first five words. In late kindergarten and early first grade classrooms, call out at least 15 words so that you sample digraphs and blends; use the entire list for late first, second, and third grades. If any students spell more than 20 words correctly, you may want to use the Elementary Spelling Inventory.

1. fan — I could use a fan on a hot day. *fan*
2. pet — I have a pet cat who likes to play. *pet*
3. dig — He will dig a hole in the sand. *dig*
4. rob — A raccoon will rob a bird's nest for eggs. *rob*
5. hope — I hope you will do well on this test. *hope*
6. wait — You will need to wait for the letter. *wait*
7. gum — I stepped on some bubble gum. *gum*
8. sled — The dog sled was pulled by huskies. *sled*
9. stick — I used a stick to poke in the hole. *stick*
10. shine — He rubbed the coin to make it shine. *shine*
11. dream — I had a funny dream last night. *dream*
12. blade — The blade of the knife was very sharp. *blade*
13. coach — The coach called the team off the field. *coach*
14. fright — She was a fright in her Halloween costume. *fright*
15. chewed — The dog chewed on the bone until it was gone. *chewed*
16. crawl — You will get dirty if you crawl under the bed. *crawl*
17. wishes — In fairy tales wishes often come true. *wishes*
18. thorn — The thorn from the rosebush stuck me. *thorn*
19. shouted — They shouted at the barking dog. *shouted*
20. spoil — The food will spoil if it sits out too long. *spoil*
21. growl — The dog will growl if you bother him. *growl*
22. third — I was the third person in line. *third*
23. camped — We camped down by the river last weekend. *camped*
24. tries — He tries hard every day to finish his work. *tries*
25. clapping — The audience was clapping after the program. *clapping*
26. riding — They are riding their bikes to the park today. *riding*

Words Their Way Primary Spelling Inventory Feature Guide

Student's Name ____________ Teacher ____________ Grade ______ Date ______

Words Spelled Correctly: ____/26 *Feature Points:* ____/56 *Total:* ____/82 *Spelling Stage:* ____________

SPELLING STAGES →	EMERGENT LATE	LETTER NAME-ALPHABETIC EARLY		MIDDLE	LATE	WITHIN WORD PATTERN EARLY	MIDDLE	LATE	SYLLABLES AND AFFIXES EARLY		
Features →	**Consonants Initial**	**Consonants Final**	**Short Vowels**	**Digraphs**	**Blends**	**Long Vowel Patterns**	**Other Vowels**	**Inflected Endings**	**Feature Points**	**Words Spelled Correctly**
1. fan	f	n	a							
2. pet	p	t	e							
3. dig	d	g	i							
4. rob	r	b	o							
5. hope	h	p				o-e				
6. wait	w	t				ai				
7. gum	g	m	u							
8. sled			e		sl					
9. stick			i		st					
10. shine				sh		i-e				
11. dream					dr	ea				
12. blade					bl	a-e				
13. coach				-ch		oa				
14. fright					fr	igh				
15. chewed				ch			ew	-ed		
16. crawl					cr		aw			
17. wishes				-sh				-es		
18. thorn				th			or			

(continued)

Words Their Way Primary Spelling Inventory Feature Guide

Student's Name ______________ Teacher ______________ Grade ________ Date ________

Words Spelled Correctly: _____ */26* *Feature Points:* _____ */56* *Total:* _____ */82* *Spelling Stage:* ____________

SPELLING STAGES →	EMERGENT LATE / LETTER NAME-ALPHABETIC EARLY			LETTER NAME-ALPHABETIC MIDDLE	LETTER NAME-ALPHABETIC LATE / WITHIN WORD PATTERN EARLY		WITHIN WORD PATTERN MIDDLE	WITHIN WORD PATTERN LATE / SYLLABLES AND AFFIXES EARLY		
Features →	**Consonants Initial**	**Consonants Final**	**Short Vowels**	**Digraphs**	**Blends**	**Long Vowel Patterns**	**Other Vowels**	**Inflected Endings**	**Feature Points**	**Words Spelled Correctly**
19. shouted				sh			ou	-ed		
20. spoil							oi			
21. growl							ow			
22. third				th			ir			
23. camped								-ed		
24. tries					tr			-ies		
25. clapping								-pping		
26. riding								-ding		
Totals	/7	/7	/7	/7	/7	/7	/7	/7	/56	/26

Words Their Way Primary Spelling Inventory Classroom Composite

Teacher ______________ School ______________ Grade ______________ Date ______________

SPELLING STAGES →	EMERGENT LATE	LETTER NAME-ALPHABETIC EARLY	MIDDLE	LATE	WITHIN WORD PATTERN EARLY	MIDDLE	LATE	SYLLABLES AND AFFIXES EARLY		
Students' Name	Consonants		Short Vowels	Digraphs	Blends	Long Vowels	Other Vowels	Inflected Endings	Correct Spelling	Total Rank Order
	Initial	Final								
Possible Points	7	7	7	7	7	7	7	7	26	82
1.										
2.										
3.										
4.										
5.										
6.										
7.										
8.										
9.										
10.										
11.										
12.										
13.										
14.										
15.										
16.										
17.										
18.										
19.										

(continued)

Words Their Way Primary Spelling Inventory Classroom Composite

Teacher ______________ School ______________ Grade __________ Date __________

SPELLING STAGES →	EMERGENT LATE	LETTER NAME-ALPHABETIC EARLY	MIDDLE	LATE	WITHIN WORD PATTERN EARLY	MIDDLE	LATE	SYLLABLES AND AFFIXES EARLY		
↓ Students' Name	Consonants		Short Vowels	Digraphs	Blends	Long Vowels	Other Vowels	Inflected Endings	Correct Spelling	Total Rank Order
	Initial	Final								
Possible Points	7	7	7	7	7	7	7	7	26	82
20.										
21.										
22.										
23.										
24.										
25.										
26.										
Highlight for Instruction*										

*Highlight students who miss more than 1 on a particular feature; they will benefit from more instruction in that area.

Elementary Spelling Inventory (ESI)

The Elementary Spelling Inventory (ESI) covers more stages than the PSI. It can be used as early as first grade, particularly if a school system wants to use the same inventory across the elementary grades. The 25 words are ordered by difficulty to sample features of the letter name-alphabetic to derivational relations stages. Call out enough words so that you have at least five or six misspelled words to analyze. If any students spell more than 20 words correctly, use the Upper Level Spelling Inventory.

1. bed	I hopped out of bed this morning. *bed*
2. ship	The ship sailed around the island. *ship*
3. when	When will you come back? *when*
4. lump	He had a lump on his head after he fell. *lump*
5. float	I can float on the water with my new raft. *float*
6. train	I rode the train to the next town. *train*
7. place	I found a new place to put my books. *place*
8. drive	I learned to drive a car. *drive*
9. bright	The light is very bright. *bright*
10. shopping	She went shopping for new shoes. *shopping*
11. spoil	The food will spoil if it is not kept cool. *spoil*
12. serving	The restaurant is serving dinner tonight. *serving*
13. chewed	The dog chewed up my favorite sweater yesterday. *chewed*
14. carries	She carries apples in her basket. *carries*
15. marched	We marched in the parade. *marched*
16. shower	The shower in the bathroom was very hot. *shower*
17. bottle	The bottle broke into pieces on the tile floor. *bottle*
18. favor	He did his brother a favor by taking out the trash. *favor*
19. ripen	The fruit will ripen over the next few days. *ripen*
20. cellar	I went down to the cellar for the can of paint. *cellar*
21. pleasure	It was a pleasure to listen to the choir sing. *pleasure*
22. fortunate	It was fortunate that the driver had snow tires. *fortunate*
23. confident	I am confident that we can win the game. *confident*
24. civilize	They wanted to civilize the forest people. *civilize*
25. opposition	The coach said the opposition would be tough. *opposition*

Words Their Way Elementary Spelling Inventory Feature

Student's Name ______________ Teacher ______________ Grade ________ Date ________

Words Spelled Correctly:_____/25 Feature Points:_____/62 Total:_____/87 Spelling Stage:________

SPELLING STAGES →	EMERGENT LATE	LETTER NAME-ALPHABETIC EARLY		MIDDLE	LATE	WITHIN WORD PATTERN EARLY	MIDDLE	LATE	SYLLABLES AND AFFIXES EARLY	MIDDLE	LATE	DERIVATIONAL RELATIONS EARLY	MIDDLE		
Features →	Consonants Initial	Consonants Final	Short Vowels	Digraphs	Blends	Long Vowels	Other Vowels	Inflected Endings	Syllable Junctures	Unaccented Final Syllables	Harder Suffixes	Bases or Roots	Feature Points	Words Spelled Correctly
1. bed	b	d	e											
2. ship		p	i	sh										
3. when			e	wh										
4. lump	l		u		mp									
5. float		t			fl	oa								
6. train		n			tr	ai								
7. place					pl	a-e								
8. drive		v			dr	i-e								
9. bright					br	igh								
10. shopping			o	sh				pping						
11. spoil					sp		oi							
12. serving							er	ving						
13. chewed				ch			ew	ed						
14. carries							ar	ies	rr					
15. marched				ch			ar	ed						
16. shower				sh			ow			er				
17. bottle									tt	le				
18. favor									v	or				

(continued)

Words Their Way Elementary Spelling Inventory Feature

Student's Name ______________ Teacher ______________ Grade ________ Date ________

Words Spelled Correctly:_____/25 Feature Points:_____/62 Total:_____/87 Spelling Stage:___________

SPELLING STAGES →	EMERGENT LATE	LETTER NAME-ALPHABETIC EARLY	MIDDLE		LATE	WITHIN WORD PATTERN EARLY	MIDDLE	LATE	SYLLABLES AND AFFIXES EARLY	MIDDLE	LATE	DERIVATIONAL RELATIONS EARLY	MIDDLE		
Features →	Consonants Initial	Consonants Final	Short Vowels	Digraphs	Blends	Long Vowels	Other Vowels	Inflected Endings	Syllable Junctures	Unaccented Final Syllables	Harder Suffixes	Bases or Roots	Feature Points	Words Spelled Correctly
19. ripen									p	en				
20. cellar									ll	ar				
21. pleasure											ure	pleas		
22. fortunate							or				ate	fortun		
23. confident											ent	confid		
24. civilize											ize	civil		
25. opposition											tion	pos		
Totals		/7	/5	/6	/7	/5	/7	/5	/5	/5	/5	/5	/62	/25

Words Their Way Elementary Spelling Inventory Classroom Composite

Teacher ______________ School ______________ Grade ________ Date ________

SPELLING STAGES →	EMERGENT LATE / LETTER NAME-ALPHABETIC EARLY	LETTER NAME-ALPHABETIC MIDDLE		LETTER NAME-ALPHABETIC LATE / WITHIN WORD PATTERN EARLY	WITHIN WORD PATTERN MIDDLE	WITHIN WORD PATTERN LATE	SYLLABLES AND AFFIXES EARLY	SYLLABLES AND AFFIXES MIDDLE	SYLLABLES AND AFFIXES LATE	DERIVATIONAL RELATIONS EARLY	DERIVATIONAL RELATIONS MIDDLE		
↓ Students' Names	Consonants	Short Vowels	Digraphs	Blends	Long Vowels	Other Vowels	Inflected Endings	Syllable Junctures	Unaccented Final Syllables	Harder Suffixes	Bases or Roots	Correct Spelling	Total Rank Order
Possible Points	7	5	6	7	5	7	5	5	5	5	5	25	87
1.													
2.													
3.													
4.													
5.													
6.													
7.													
8.													
9.													
10.													
11.													
12.													
13.													
14.													
15.													
16.													
17.													
18.													
19.													

(continued)

Words Their Way Elementary Spelling Inventory Classroom Composite

Teacher ______________ School ______________ Grade __________ Date __________

SPELLING STAGES →	EMERGENT LATE / LETTER NAME-ALPHABETIC EARLY		LETTER NAME-ALPHABETIC MIDDLE	LETTER NAME-ALPHABETIC LATE	WITHIN WORD PATTERN EARLY	WITHIN WORD PATTERN MIDDLE	WITHIN WORD PATTERN LATE	SYLLABLES AND AFFIXES EARLY	SYLLABLES AND AFFIXES MIDDLE	SYLLABLES AND AFFIXES LATE / DERIVATIONAL RELATIONS EARLY	DERIVATIONAL RELATIONS MIDDLE		
↓ Students' Names	Consonants	Short Vowels	Digraphs	Blends	Long Vowels	Other Vowels	Inflected Endings	Syllable Junctures	Unaccented Final Syllables	Harder Suffixes	Bases or Roots	Correct Spelling	Total Rank Order
Possible Points	7	5	6	7	5	7	5	5	5	5	5	25	87
20.													
21.													
22.													
23.													
24.													
25.													
Highlight for Instruction*													

Note: *Highlight students who miss more than 1 on a particular feature; they will benefit from more instruction in that area.

Upper-Level Spelling Inventory (USI)

The Upper-Level Spelling Inventory (USI) can be used in upper elementary. middle, high school, and postsecondary classrooms. The 31 words are ordered by difficulty to sample features of the within word pattern to derivational relations spelling stages. With normally achieving students, you can administer the entire list, but you may stop when students misspell more than eight words and are experiencing noticeable frustration. If any students misspell five of the first eight words, use the ESI to more accurately identify within word pattern features that need instruction.

1. switch	We can switch television channels with a remote control. *switch*
2. smudge	There was a smudge on the mirror from her fingertips. *smudge*
3. trapped	He was trapped in the elevator when the electricity went off. *trapped*
4. scrape	The fall caused her to scrape her knee. *scrape*
5. knotted	The knotted rope would not come undone. *knotted*
6. shaving	He didn't start shaving with a razor until 11th grade. *shaving*
7. squirt	Don't let the ketchup squirt out of the bottle too fast. *squirt*
8. pounce	My cat likes to pounce on her toy mouse. *pounce*
9. scratches	We had to paint over the scratches on the car. *scratches*
10. crater	The crater of the volcano was filled with bubbling lava. *crater*
11. sailor	When he was young. he wanted to go to sea as a sailor. *sailor*
12. village	My Granddad lived in a small seaside village. *village*
13. disloyal	Traitors are disloyal to their country. *disloyal*
14. tunnel	The rockslide closed the tunnel through the mountain. *tunnel*
15. humor	You need a sense of humor to understand his jokes. *humor*
16. confidence	With each winning game, the team's confidence grew. *confidence*

17.	fortunate	The driver was fortunate to have snow tires on that winter day. *fortunate*
18.	visible	The singer on the stage was visible to everyone. *visible*
19.	circumference	The length of the equator is equal to the circumference of the earth. *circumference*
20.	civilization	We studied the ancient Mayan civilization last year. *civilization*
21.	monarchy	A monarchy is headed by a king or a queen. *monarchy*
22.	dominance	The dominance of the Yankee's baseball team lasted for several years. *dominance*
23.	correspond	Many students correspond through e-mail. *correspond*
24.	illiterate	It is hard to get a job if you are illiterate. *illiterate*
25.	emphasize	I want to emphasize the importance of trying your best. *emphasize*
26.	opposition	The coach said the opposition would give us a tough game. *opposition*
27.	chlorine	My eyes were burning from the chlorine in the swimming pool. *chlorine*
28.	commotion	The audience heard the commotion backstage. *commotion*
29.	medicinal	Cough drops are to be taken for medicinal purposes only. *medicinal*
30.	irresponsible	It is irresponsible not to wear a seat belt. *irresponsible*
31.	succession	The firecrackers went off in rapid succession. *succession*

Words Their Way Upper-Level Spelling Inventory Feature Guide

Student's Name ____________ Teacher ____________ Grade ______ Date ______

Words Spelled Correctly:_____/31 Feature Points:_____/68 Total:_____/99 Spelling Stage:__________

SPELLING STAGES →	WITHIN WORD PATTERN EARLY MIDDLE		LATE	SYLLABLES AND AFFIXES EARLY	MIDDLE	LATE	DERIVATIONAL RELATIONS EARLY	MIDDLE	LATE		
Features →	**Blends and Digraphs**	**Vowels**	**Complex Consonants**	**Inflected Endings and Syllable Juncture**	**Unaccented Final Syllable**	**Affixes**	**Reduced Vowels in Unaccented Syllables**	**Greek and Latin Elements**	**Assimilated Prefixes**	**Feature Points**	**Words Spelled Correctly**
1. switch	sw	i	tch								
2. smudge	sm	u	dge								
3. trapped	tr			pped							
4. scrape		a-e	scr								
5. knotted		o	kn	tted							
6. shaving	sh			ving							
7. squirt		ir	squ								
8. pounce		ou	ce								
9. scratches		a	tch	es							
10. crater	cr			t	er						
11. sailor		ai			or						
12. village				ll	age						
13. disloyal		oy			al	dis					
14. tunnel				nn	el						
15. humor				m	or						
16. confidence						con	fid				
17. fortunate					ate			fortun			
Subtotals	/5	/9	/7	/8	/7	/2	/1	/1	/0	/40	/17

(continued)

Words Their Way Upper-Level Spelling Inventory Feature Guide

Student's Name ____________ Teacher ____________ Grade ______ Date ______

Words Spelled Correctly:____/31 Feature Points:____/68 Total:____/99 Spelling Stage:______

SPELLING STAGES →	WITHIN WORD PATTERN EARLY MIDDLE		LATE	SYLLABLES AND AFFIXES EARLY	MIDDLE	LATE	DERIVATIONAL RELATIONS EARLY	MIDDLE	LATE		
Features →	**Blends and Digraphs**	**Vowels**	**Complex Consonants**	**Inflected Endings and Syllable Juncture**	**Unaccented Final Syllable**	**Affixes**	**Reduced Vowels in Unaccented Syllables**	**Greek and Latin Elements**	**Assimilated Prefixes**	**Feature Points**	**Words Spelled Correctly**
18. visible						ible		vis			
19. circumference						ence		circum			
20. civilization							liz	civil			
21. monarchy								arch			
22. dominance						ance	min				
23. correspond							res		rr		
24. illiterate					ate				ll		
25. emphasize						size	pha				
26. opposition							pos		pp		
27. chlorine						ine		chlor			
28. commotion						tion			mm		
29. medicinal					al			medic			
30. irresponsible						ible	res		rr		
31. succession						sion			cc		
Subtotals	/0	/0	/0	/0	/2	/8	/6	/6	/6	/28	/14
Totals*	**/5**	**/9**	**/7**	**/8**	**/9**	**/10**	**/7**	**/7**	**/6**	**/68**	**/31**

Words Their Way Upper-Level Spelling Inventory Classroom Composite

Teacher ______________ School ______________ Grade __________ Date __________

SPELLING STAGES →	WITHIN WORD PATTERN EARLY MIDDLE LATE			SYLLABLES AND AFFIXES EARLY MIDDLE LATE			DERIVATIONAL RELATIONS EARLY MIDDLE LATE			
↓ Students' Names	Blends and Digraphs	Vowels	Complex Consonants	Inflected Endings and Syllable Junctures	Unaccented Final Syllables	Affixes	Reduced Vowels in Unaccented Syllables	Greek and Latin Elements	Assimilated Prefixes	Total Rank Order
Possible Points	5	9	7	8	9	10	7	7	6	99
1.										
2.										
3.										
4.										
5.										
6.										
7.										
8.										
9.										
10.										
11.										
12.										
13.										
14.										
15.										
16.										
17.										
18.										
19.										

(continued)

Words Their Way Upper-Level Spelling Inventory Classroom Composite

Teacher ______________ School ______________ Grade ________ Date ________

SPELLING STAGES →	WITHIN WORD PATTERN EARLY MIDDLE LATE		SYLLABLES AND AFFIXES EARLY MIDDLE LATE			DERIVATIONAL RELATIONS EARLY MIDDLE LATE				
↓ Students' Names	Blends and Digraphs	Vowels	Complex Consonants	Inflected Endings and Syllable Junctures	Unaccented Final Syllables	Affixes	Reduced Vowels in Unaccented Syllables	Greek and Latin Elements	Assimilated Prefixes	Total Rank Order
Possible Points	**5**	**9**	**7**	**8**	**9**	**10**	**7**	**7**	**6**	**99**
20.										
21.										
22.										
23.										
24.										
25.										
26.										
27.										
Highlight for Instruction*										

*Highlight students who miss more than 1 on a particular feature if tried total is between 5 and 8. Highlight those who miss more than 2 if the total is between 9 and 10.

K–8 Diagnostic Assessment

Vocabulary

- **Critchlow Verbal Language Scales**

Critchlow Verbal Language Scales

SKILL ASSESSED
Vocabulary

Grade Level
K–8

Language
- English

Grouping
Individual

Approximate Testing Time
15 Minutes

Materials
- English Record Form (p. 3)

Source
From *Dos Amigos Verbal Language Scales* by Donald E. Critchlow.

WHAT The *Critchlow Verbal Language Scales* assess a student's vocabulary in English. Vocabulary is assessed by asking a student to say the "opposite" of a series of words spoken by the examiner. The words on this assessment are arranged in increasing order of difficulty. The scale contains 75 English stimulus words.

WHY As students progress through the grades, they build larger and larger vocabularies. A more advanced vocabulary enables students to better comprehend what they read and hear as well as to better express their thoughts. Measuring vocabulary provides an index of what a student has learned and how well equipped the student is for future learning.

HOW Before beginning the test, determine that the student understands what an opposite is and can demonstrate this knowledge. For example say: "If it is not daytime, it is ________" or "If a child is not a boy, it is a ________" to help establish the concept of opposite.

Explain to the student that you are going to say a word and he or she is to respond with the opposite of that word. Begin with item 1 for all students, and discontinue testing after the child misses five consecutive words or completes the scale. Do not give credit for a response that is not listed.

Note that alternatives are sometimes provided for a stimulus or acceptable response. For example, the response to *absent* is listed as *present-here,* indicating that either response is correct.

WHAT IT MEANS Count the number correct and refer to the scoring criteria below to identify the approximate vocabulary grade level. For students who score below their current grade level, provide direct instruction in specific vocabulary needed for school success.

Number Correct English	Vocabulary Grade Level
1–8	Grade K and below
9–12	Grade 1
13–17	Grade 2
18–21	Grade 3
22–26	Grade 4
27–30	Grade 5
31–34	Grade 6
35 and above	Grade 7 and above

WHAT'S NEXT? For students with limited vocabulary, more intense support in developing other underlying reading skills may be warranted. Further testing of fluency, phonics, or phoneme segmentation ability may be indicated.

Critchlow Verbal Language Scale

Name: ______________________ **Grade:** __________ **Date:** __________

Directions: Ask the student to say the opposite of each word. Discontinue testing after five consecutive errors.

	STIMULUS	RESPONSE		STIMULUS	RESPONSE
_____	1. boy	girl	_____	39. multiply	divide
_____	2. up	down	_____	40. friend	enemy
_____	3. front	back	_____	41. difficult	easy
_____	4. hot	cold	_____	42. narrow	wide
_____	5. brother	sister	_____	43. wild	tame
_____	6. dirty	clean	_____	44. dangerous	safe
_____	7. wet	dry	_____	45. entrance	exit
_____	8. crooked	straight	_____	46. sharp	dull
_____	9. young	old	_____	47. imprisoned	free
_____	10. off	on	_____	48. falsehood	truth
_____	11. shut	open	_____	49. public	private
_____	12. noisy	quiet	_____	50. costly	cheap
_____	13. dead	alive	_____	51. lengthen	shorten
_____	14. early	late	_____	52. succeed	fail
_____	15. empty	full	_____	53. victory	defeat
_____	16. near	far	_____	54. stale	fresh
_____	17. come	go	_____	55. timid	bold-brave
_____	18. north	south	_____	56. maximum	minimum
_____	19. lost	found	_____	57. unite	separate
_____	20. pretty	ugly-homely	_____	58. profit	loss
_____	21. sick	well	_____	59. complex	simple
_____	22. sour	sweet	_____	60. create	destroy
_____	23. add	subtract	_____	61. vertical	horizontal
_____	24. daughter	son	_____	62. former	latter
_____	25. remember	forget	_____	63. bless	curse
_____	26. false	true	_____	64. loiter	hurry
_____	27. love	hate	_____	65. discord	harmony
_____	28. heavy	light	_____	66. gradual	sudden
_____	29. tight	loose	_____	67. diminish	increase
_____	30. after	before	_____	68. naive	sophisticated
_____	31. laugh	cry	_____	69. superfluous	necessary
_____	32. smooth	rough	_____	70. asset	liability
_____	33. absent	present-here	_____	71. tentative	permanent
_____	34. strong	weak	_____	72. clergy	laity
_____	35. evening	morning	_____	73. corpulent	slender
_____	36. raw	cooked	_____	74. epilogue	prologue
_____	37. begin	end-stop	_____	75. autocracy	democracy
_____	38. same	different			

Score: _____ /75

K–8 Diagnostic Assessment

Reading Comprehension

- **Leveled Passages Placement Grades K–8**
- **Metacomprehension Strategy Index**
- **McLeod Assessment of Reading Comprehension**

Leveled Passages Grades K-8

▶ **WHAT** The *Leveled Passages Placement Assessment* tests overall reading comprehension and grade-level reading proficiency. Students read a series of passages that get progressively harder and answer accompanying comprehension questions. There is one set of passages and questions for each grade level. It is useful to test frequently in the elementary and middle school grades.

▶ **WHY** Comprehension is the ultimate goal of reading. This assessment requires students to accurately decode words, to apply their knowledge of vocabulary, and to use critical reading strategies that aid in the literal and inferential comprehension of what is read. When administered to everyone in a class, the assessment serves as a valuable screening for identifying students who may have reading difficulties and who may benefit from additional assessment that focuses on specific skills underlying reading. It can also be used to place students in appropriate-leveled materials to work on critical prerequisite skills and to build overall reading fluency. Since the goal of all instruction is access to core, grade-level content and reading materials, students should only use lower-level materials as needed to work on targeted skills. They should also have exposure to grade-level text and receive ample preteaching and reteaching during small group instructional periods to access this material.

▶ **HOW** Make booklets for students by copying the passages and questions in grade-level order. Begin with passages two grade levels below the students' current grade and end two grade levels above the current grade (if applicable). For example, a grade 4 student would receive a booklet containing grades 2–6 passages and questions. Distribute the booklets to the students.

Explain to students that this test will help you find the best reading level for them so that they can enjoy reading and build their reading skills. Make sure students are sitting in a comfortable setting with minimal distractions, and encourage them to do their best on the test.

In order to administer the test efficiently and make the directions understandable, you should be familiar with the directions and the test items before the test is given. During the administration, monitor students closely to make sure that each student is following the directions, is on the correct item, and is marking the test form correctly.

▶ WHAT IT MEANS The assessment can be scored using the Answer Key at the end of this section (page 60). It lists the correct response for each question. Mark each incorrect item on the student's test, and record the number of correct items. To find the percentage for each score, use the Scoring Chart at the end of this section (page 61).

If students achieve a score of 80%–90%, then they should receive instruction on that grade level. If students receive a score below 80%, then administer additional assessments to determine specific skill needs. These students may need targeted skills-based instruction during small group time to build mastery of prerequisite skills. These students may struggle with grade-level text and will need ample preteaching and reteaching of core content. If students score higher than 90%, monitor their progress in the weeks following the assessment. You might consider providing advanced, or beyond-level, instruction and practice to accelerate their reading growth and enrich the grade-level activities provided.

Directions:

Give the child a copy of the Comprehension section of the test. Read the story and the questions aloud. The child will answer the question by marking the answers.

Now I am going to read you a story. Listen to the story. Then I will ask you some questions. Here is the story.

The Amazing Fish

One day, a fisherman caught an amazing fish with his fishing pole. The fish asked to be let go. "I will grant you three wishes if you let me go," the fish said.

"Very well, said the fisherman. "I wish to be a king."

The fish granted the fisherman's first wish, but the fisherman was not happy.

"I wish for a castle," said the fisherman. So the fish granted the fisherman's second wish, but the fisherman was not happy.

"I wish for a bigger castle," said the fisherman. "I want one that reaches up to the sun!"

"That is not possible," said the fish. "Wish again."

The fisherman became very angry and stomped his foot. "Oh, how I wish I had never met you!" he screamed.

So the fish granted the fisherman's last wish. In an instant, the fisherman was no longer a king with a castle. He was a fisherman fishing in the sea.

Now I will read some questions.

Have the child look at page 6.

1. *Point to the star. Look at the pictures. Which picture shows what the fisherman wished for first? Circle the picture.*

2. *Point to the sun. Look at the pictures. Which picture shows what happened to the fisherman at the end of the story? Circle the picture.*

Have the child look at page 7.

3. *Point to the circle. Look at the pictures. Which picture shows what the fisherman wanted his castle to reach up to? Circle the picture.*

4. *Point to the triangle. Look at the pictures. Which picture shows something the fisherman used to catch fish? Circle the picture.*

Have the child look at page 8.

5. *Point to the moon. Look at the pictures. Which picture shows something that could **not** really happen? Circle the picture.*

6. *Point to the square. Look at the pictures. Which picture shows what will happen to the fisherman next? Circle the picture.*

Comprehension

1.

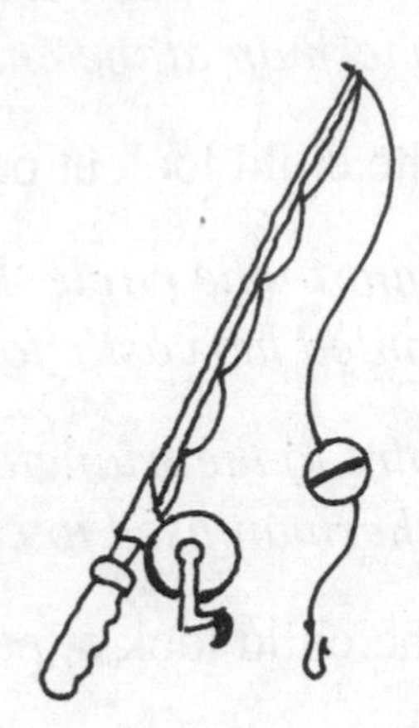

2.

Comprehension

3.

4.

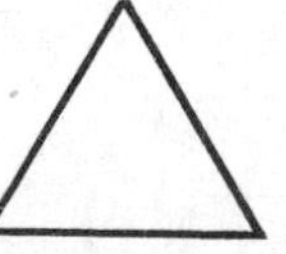

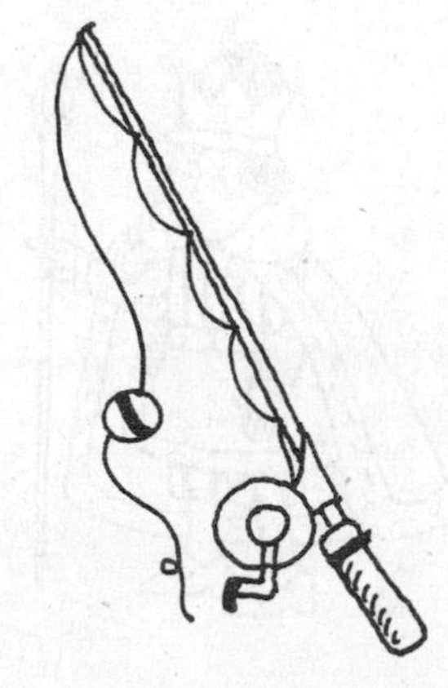

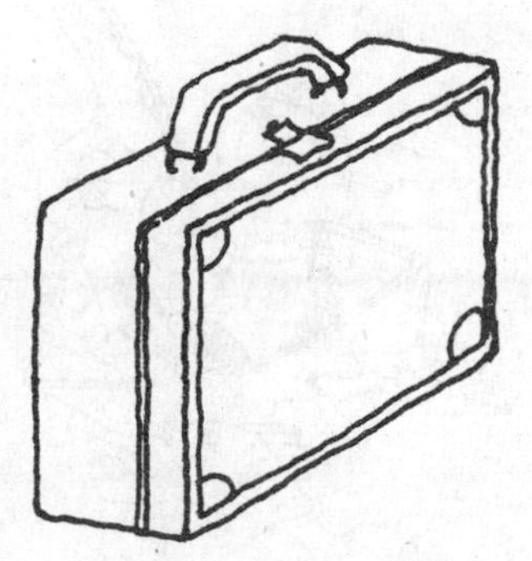

Comprehension

5. 

6. 

Directions:

Have children turn to the Comprehension section of the test. There are two reading passages in this section. You will read the passages and the questions aloud. Children will answer the questions by marking pictures.

Now I am going to read you some stories. Listen to the first story. Then I will ask you some questions. Here is the story.

Have you ever seen a real bear? Most bears live in the mountains or the forest. Bears like to eat many different foods. They eat lots of nuts and berries. Some bears catch and eat fish from the rivers. One of the bear's favorite foods is honey, which is made by bees. The bear finds a beehive and takes the honey.

All through the summer, bears eat a lot and get very big. When fall comes, the weather gets colder. When the leaves fall off the trees, the bear knows that winter will come soon. The bear finds a good place to go for winter, such as a cave or a hole in the ground. The bear climbs in and goes to sleep for the winter. In the spring, the bear will wake up and start eating again.

Now I will read some questions.

1. *Point to the star at the top of the page. Look at the pictures. What is the story mostly about? Fill in the circle under the picture that shows what the story is mostly about.*
2. *Point to the moon. Which picture shows where a bear gets honey? Fill in the circle under the picture that shows where the bear gets honey.*
3. *Point to the sun. Which picture shows how the bear knows when winter is coming? Fill in the circle under the picture that shows how the bear knows that winter is coming.*
4. *Point to the heart. Which picture shows where a bear likes to sleep for the winter? Fill in the circle under the picture that shows where a bear likes to sleep.*

Have children turn to the next page.

Now I am going to read another story. Listen carefully. Here is the story.

Working with Mom

Maya and Sam were excited about spending the day at the flower shop with their moms. Maya and Sam were best friends. Their families lived in the same apartment building, and their moms worked together in the same flower shop.

On Saturday morning, the four of them rode the bus together to the shop. When they got there, Maya's mom opened the door with a key. When the door opened, a little bell jingled.

"That bell will let us know when someone comes to buy something," said Sam's mom.

A minute later, the bell jingled. The first customer walked in.

"Hello, may I help you?" asked Maya's mom.

The man told them he would like a bouquet of fresh flowers.

"We'll make that for you, and it will be beautiful," said Maya's mom. "We have lots of help today."

Sam and Maya helped their moms choose the flowers. Sam's mom snipped the stems and put everything into a vase. "It's so pretty," said Maya.

The man was happy, too. "I think you should let these two come to work with you more often!" he said, smiling at Maya and Sam.

Maya and Sam were happy with the work they had done.

Now I will read some questions.

5. *Point to the star at the top of the page. Look at the pictures. Which picture shows what this story is mostly about? Fill in the circle under the picture.*

6. *Point to the moon. Which picture shows how Maya and Sam and their moms got to work? Fill in the circle under the picture that shows how they got to work.*

7. *Point to the sun. Which picture shows something that happens at the beginning of the story? Fill in the circle under the picture that shows something that happens at the beginning of the story.*

8. *Point to the heart. Which picture best shows how the two families feel about each other? Fill in the circle under the picture that best shows how the two families feel about each other.*

Comprehension

Comprehension

Directions:

Have children turn to the Comprehension section of the test. Then give them these directions.

This part of the test has two reading passages and 10 questions. Read each passage and answer the questions that follow. Mark your answers.

Have children read the passages and answer questions 1–10 independently.

Comprehension

Read this story about a girl named Kate. Then answer questions 1–5. Mark your answers.

On the Train

Kate could hardly keep her eyes open. She was trying to read. She was sitting on the train beside her brother Jed. Mom and Dad were sitting one row behind them. They were all going to Baltimore to visit Grandpa. Kate picked up her book again. Her eyes still would not stay open. She was so tired that she fell asleep. Soon she began to dream. She dreamed that a funny thing happened. She looked at the seat next to her. Jed was not there. Instead, a bear was sitting in the seat. It was a trained bear from a circus.

"How did you get here?" asked Kate. "Who are you, and where's Jed?"

"My name is Belle," said the bear. "Jed and I traded places. He is working at the circus now. I am going to Baltimore with you."

"Oh, but I miss my brother," said Kate. "We must bring him back."

"That's okay with me," said Belle. "I miss my friends at the circus, too."

Kate and Belle made the train stop. Then they got off the train. They went to the circus. Jed was there. He was trying to ride a bear's funny bike.

"Boy, am I glad to see you," said Jed. "Being in the circus is not much fun. Besides, I can't ride this silly bike."

"That bike is not silly," said Belle. "That is my bike."

Belle climbed on the bike. She began to ride around. She waved at all her friends. She seemed happy to be back at the circus. Kate looked at Jed and said, "Let's go back to the train."

"You bet!" said Jed.

Just then, Kate woke up. She looked at the seat beside her. Jed was there reading his book.

"What a funny dream," thought Kate.

1. What happened to Kate in this story?
   Ⓐ She got a job at the circus.
   Ⓑ She fell off a bike.
   Ⓒ She changed her name to Belle.
   Ⓓ She had a dream.

2. Why were Jed and Kate going to Baltimore?
   Ⓐ They were going to visit Grandpa.
   Ⓑ They wanted to join a circus.
   Ⓒ They were going to see Belle.
   Ⓓ They wanted to visit Mom and Dad.

3. How did Kate feel when she saw Belle in the seat beside her?
   Ⓐ upset
   Ⓑ glad
   Ⓒ angry
   Ⓓ surprised

4. What can you tell about Belle?
   Ⓐ She works in a circus.
   Ⓑ She wants to go to Baltimore.
   Ⓒ She knows Grandpa.
   Ⓓ She does not like trains.

5. What happened last?
   Ⓐ Belle got off the train.
   Ⓑ Kate woke up.
   Ⓒ Jed went to the circus.
   Ⓓ Kate got on the train.

Comprehension

Read this passage about a pony. Then answer questions 6–10. Mark your answers.

Gentle Friends

Have you ever heard of a Shetland pony? Ponies are very small horses. The Shetland pony is the smallest horse of all. The largest Shetland pony is less than four feet tall. The smallest may only grow to about two feet tall. That is a lot shorter than a boy or girl in second grade!

Shetland ponies come from the Shetland Islands near Scotland. These islands can be very cold. Shetland ponies have very long hair. Their hair can have many shades of color. Most of the ponies have patches of black and white.

Shetland ponies are very strong. Long ago, they worked in coal mines. Coal mines are places where people dig coal out of the ground. The ponies were small enough to go into the mines. They were also strong enough to pull wagons filled with coal.

Children love Shetland ponies because they are very calm. They never get upset. Did you ever go on a pony ride? If you did, you most likely rode a Shetland pony.

Today, some Shetland ponies work on farms. Most of them are pets or horses kept for show. Do you think you would like to have a Shetland pony?

6. What is this passage MOSTLY about?

   Ⓐ coal mines

   Ⓑ farms in Scotland

   Ⓒ Shetland ponies

   Ⓓ children and their pets

7. Why were Shetland ponies good for working in coal mines?

   Ⓐ They are small and strong.

   Ⓑ They are easy to train.

   Ⓒ They can see in the dark.

   Ⓓ They can smell coal.

8. Shetland ponies probably have long hair to
   - Ⓐ look nice.
   - Ⓑ keep warm.
   - Ⓒ change colors.
   - Ⓓ stay clean.

9. From this passage, what can you tell about coal mines?
   - Ⓐ They have lots of light.
   - Ⓑ They do not have much room.
   - Ⓒ They are very clean.
   - Ⓓ They do not have any coal left.

10. Shetland ponies are used to give pony rides because they
   - Ⓐ come from islands near Scotland.
   - Ⓑ have long hair.
   - Ⓒ may be almost any color.
   - Ⓓ are very gentle.

Comprehension

Read each passage and answer the questions that follow.

Friends

One day, a young bear, a beaver, and a raccoon were playing hide-and-seek in the woods. A small brown rabbit came hopping down the path and asked to play.

"Sure," said the bear, "you can join us."

"Let's play catch," said Rabbit.

"Oh, but we're playing hide-and-seek," said Beaver. Bear looked at Beaver. "All right, we'll play catch," Beaver agreed.

The animals had not played catch for very long before Rabbit demanded, "Let's play leapfrog!"

"We're playing catch," said Raccoon.

"I'm tired of playing catch," moaned Rabbit.

"Okay," said Bear, who was a bit upset but wanted to be nice to their new friend. The animals switched to leapfrog, but not for long. Rabbit soon complained, "I'm sick of this game. Let's play tag!"

Beaver had had enough. He said, "I have to go home now." Then he turned and walked away.

"I think I hear my mom calling. See you later!" said Bear, who headed toward the hills.

"I have to go, too," said Raccoon.

Rabbit was left all alone.

Third Grade Comprehension Questions – Friends

1. Where does this story take place?

   Ⓐ at school
   Ⓑ on a playground
   Ⓒ by a pond
   Ⓓ in the woods

2. What were the animals playing first?

   Ⓐ hide-and-seek
   Ⓑ catch
   Ⓒ leapfrog
   Ⓓ tag

3. Which word BEST describes Rabbit?

   Ⓐ funny
   Ⓑ selfish
   Ⓒ caring
   Ⓓ worried

4. Compare how the animals felt before Rabbit came and at the end of the story.

   Ⓐ First they were happy, then they were upset.
   Ⓑ First they were sad, then they were happy.
   Ⓒ First they were bored, then they were afraid.
   Ⓓ First they were angry, then they were sad.

5. Why did Bear say, "I think I hear my mom calling. See you later!" when Rabbit said he wanted to play tag?

   Ⓐ Bear really did hear his mom calling him for dinner.
   Ⓑ Bear was tired of switching games for Rabbit and lost interest in playing.
   Ⓒ Bear was going to secretly play a game with Rabbit after Beaver went home.
   Ⓓ Bear was going to go to Beaver's house.

Protecting the Gorillas

Forty years ago, there were not many gorillas left in Africa. Wild gorillas were being killed by hunters, and they would soon all be gone. A woman named Dian Fossey helped change that.

Dr. Fossey was from California. She was born in 1932. She loved working with animals, so she went to Africa in 1963. There she met a scientist named Dr. Louis Leakey. Dr. Leakey was studying great apes. Dian Fossey began learning about apes, too. She studied mountain gorillas.

Dr. Fossey spent some time studying gorillas in Zaire and in Rwanda. She wanted to prove that gorillas could be gentle animals, and could become friends with people. In 1967, she built a camp in the mountains called Karisoke. She lived there for a long time.

In 1970, a gorilla named Peanuts reached out and touched Dr. Fossey's hand. It was the first time a gorilla had ever touched a person in a friendly way. Before long, the wild gorillas all came to trust Dr. Fossey. This helped her understand more about the way gorillas behave. She was the first person to be this close with gorillas.

Dr. Fossey spent the rest of her life working to protect mountain gorillas. Her favorite gorilla, Digit, was killed by hunters. Dr. Fossey told the world about Digit in a story she wrote for *National Geographic* magazine. Many people read Dr. Fossey's story and wanted to send money to help protect the gorillas.

A few years later, Dr. Fossey wrote a book called *Gorillas in the Mist*, and it was made into a movie. This story of her work helped people around the world understand more about gorillas. By the early 1980's, there were about 250 wild gorillas in Africa. Dr. Fossey died in 1985, but her work lives on. Today, there are many more wild mountain gorillas. Scientists still work at Karisoke to protect the gorillas, and—thanks to Dr. Fossey—we know more about the great apes than ever before.

6. What is the MAIN idea of this passage?
   Ⓐ A gorilla named Peanuts touched Dr. Fossey's hand.
   Ⓑ Dian Fossey spent much of her life studying and protecting gorillas.
   Ⓒ Most of the gorillas in Africa were killed by hunters.
   Ⓓ Dian Fossey was born in California in 1932 and went to Africa in 1963.

7. Dian Fossey went to Africa because she wanted to
   Ⓐ work with animals.
   Ⓑ meet with Dr. Leakey.
   Ⓒ build a camp.
   Ⓓ write a magazine story.

8. Which detail shows that gorillas could be gentle and friendly to people?
   Ⓐ Dr. Fossey built a camp near the gorillas.
   Ⓑ She wrote an article about a gorilla.
   Ⓒ Peanuts touched Dr. Fossey's hand.
   Ⓓ Scientists still work at Karisoke today.

9. Why did people give money to Dr. Fossey to help the gorillas?
   Ⓐ Dr. Leakey asked people to send money.
   Ⓑ They wanted her to make a movie about gorillas.
   Ⓒ She had built a camp in the mountains.
   Ⓓ They read about her work in a magazine.

10. Why did Dr. Fossey want to live in the mountains?
    Ⓐ She loved the outdoors.
    Ⓑ She wanted to live near the gorillas.
    Ⓒ She was bored living in the city.
    Ⓓ She wanted to learn how to hunt.

Comprehension

Read each passage and answer the questions that follow.

The Animal Hunt

Yesterday was my brother Ben's fifth birthday party. As usual, since I'm the older sister, I had to help out. Mom said, "Leslie, five busy boys need to be watched carefully. You can't let them out of your sight for a minute or you'll lose one." Then she put me in charge of the games.

Since I didn't want to lose anybody, I planned only one game for the boys to play outside. Ben loved animals and looking for hidden things. So I took ten of his plastic toy animals and hid them in the vacant lot next to our apartment building. By the time I was done, there were three bears, two snakes, three monkeys, one giraffe, and one lion hidden all over the lot.

When Ben's four friends arrived for the party, I could hardly believe how noisy and excited they were. Mom said, "Leslie, I'm going to cook the pizza. You can play your game outside with the boys. Then bring them in to eat."

"Okay, Ben," I announced. "It's time to go on a safari. The boy who finds the most animals will win a prize. I have hidden ten toy animals in the empty lot. Meet me out front in one minute." The boys raced down the stairs. Then they lined up on the sidewalk ready to begin.

"On your mark, get set, go!" I cried, pointing them all toward the lot next door.

Ben and his friends tore around the lot looking under the rocks and in the grass. They shrieked and laughed as they discovered eight of the animals. Only the giraffe and a snake were still hidden. Then I noticed Chris, Ben's best friend. He was waving a snake around calling, "I found the snake!"

As I looked more closely, I knew it was not one of the thick, black, rubber snakes that I had hidden. This snake was long and thin. "Drop it, drop it!" I screamed. I had no idea whether this kind of snake was dangerous or not, but I was not going to take any chances.

Chris threw the snake up into the air. I ran over just in time to see its tail disappear under a rock. Suddenly my heart was pumping wildly. "Chris, that snake was alive! I never hid that snake. Did it bite you?" I questioned him and carefully examined his hands and arms.

He replied calmly. "No, I just picked it up and then threw it when you told me to." He looked at me and asked, "Will it count toward the prize?"

"Yes, of course," I answered, chuckling in spite of myself. Then I warned the boys, "Be careful not to pick up anything that is alive. The toy snakes are black and thick."

The rest of the game passed in slow motion for me. The boys dashed around and poked in the dirt. As soon as they uncovered the last two animals, I hurried them upstairs before anything else could happen.

Everyone agreed that Chris was the winner. He found three toy animals and one living snake!

1. Where do Ben and his sister live?
   - Ⓐ on a farm
   - Ⓑ in the woods
   - Ⓒ in an apartment building
   - Ⓓ beside a zoo
2. Which word *best* describes Ben's sister Leslie?
   - Ⓐ helpful
   - Ⓑ silly
   - Ⓒ selfish
   - Ⓓ brave
3. What happened just after Chris threw the snake into the air?
   - Ⓐ Leslie made the boys go inside.
   - Ⓑ Ben's mom made a pizza.
   - Ⓒ The boys lined up on the sidewalk.
   - Ⓓ The snake went under a rock.

4. Leslie was probably upset by the snake because she
   Ⓐ did not want one of the boys to get lost.
   Ⓑ forgot where she put it.
   Ⓒ was worried that the snake would bite Chris.
   Ⓓ did not like toy snakes.

5. Why did the rest of the game go in slow motion for Leslie?
   Ⓐ Leslie was still in shock that Chris picked up a snake.
   Ⓑ Leslie was in a trance.
   Ⓒ Leslie couldn't wait for the party to begin.
   Ⓓ Leslie was bored.

6. How was Leslie *different* after Chris picked up the snake?
   Ⓐ She did not want to help with the party anymore.
   Ⓑ She was worried about the boys.
   Ⓒ She felt more confident about herself.
   Ⓓ She thought that time went by too fast.

7. By the end of the day, what did Leslie *most likely* learn?
   Ⓐ Children like to eat pizza.
   Ⓑ Birthday parties are fun.
   Ⓒ Children do need to be watched carefully.
   Ⓓ Most birthday parties are peaceful and quiet.

Dr. Drew: A Great American

Every year, about 8 million Americans give blood to help others. This blood is saved in places called "blood banks." Then it is used to help people who are injured or become sick. How can blood be saved in a bank until it is needed? The work of an African-American man named Charles Drew made it possible.

Charles Richard Drew was born in Washington, D.C., in 1904. In school, Charles got good grades, and he was always good in sports. In high school, he was named best all-around athlete. He did especially well in track and football. He probably could have become a professional athlete, but he decided not to. When Charles was 15 years old, his sister died of tuberculosis. That is a disease of the lungs. After experiencing his sister's illness, Charles decided to become a doctor. He first attended college in Baltimore and then went to McGill University in Montreal, Canada, to become a doctor. There he met Dr. John Beattie, who was one of his teachers. Charles Drew became interested in Dr. Beattie's work with blood. He soon began reading all he could about blood. He and Dr. Beattie became good friends. They worked together until Charles finished school.

Dr. Drew continued to study blood. In 1938, he wrote an important paper called "Banked Blood." It was about the best ways to save blood in a blood bank. Drew discovered new ways to store large amounts of blood—and just in time! Drew made his discovery just when the fighting of World War II began. A lot of blood was needed to save wounded soldiers, and Dr. Drew was the man to collect it. In 1941, he became the head of the American Red Cross Blood Bank in New York. He was in charge of the blood that would be used for the U.S. Army and Navy.

Dr. Charles Drew and his work probably saved millions of lives during the war and in the years since then. He was a remarkable man. To honor Dr. Drew, the U.S. Postal Service issued a stamp with his picture on it in 1981. The stamp was part of a special series called "Great Americans."

8. What is this passage *mostly* about?
   Ⓐ a series of stamps called “Great Americans”
   Ⓑ Dr. Charles Drew and his work with blood
   Ⓒ why Dr. Drew went to school in Canada
   Ⓓ how the United States got into World War II

9. Which detail supports the idea that Charles Drew was a “Great American”?
   Ⓐ He grew up in Washington, D.C.
   Ⓑ He went to McGill University in Canada.
   Ⓒ His discovery saved millions of lives.
   Ⓓ He wrote a paper called “Banked Blood.”

10. What did Charles Drew do just after high school?
    Ⓐ He became a professional athlete.
    Ⓑ He wrote a paper about blood.
    Ⓒ He joined the U.S. Army.
    Ⓓ He went to college.

11. Charles Drew decided to become a doctor because
    Ⓐ he was not very good at sports.
    Ⓑ he lost his sister to a disease.
    Ⓒ he always got good grades in school.
    Ⓓ he knew that people needed him.

12. The purpose of this passage is to
    Ⓐ persuade people to give blood.
    Ⓑ compare Charles Drew with other doctors.
    Ⓒ give information about Charles Drew.
    Ⓓ tell an entertaining story about Charles Drew.

13. Before Dr. Charles Drew made his discovery, people did not know how to
    Ⓐ store large amounts of blood.
    Ⓑ become professional athletes.
    Ⓒ recognize different kinds of disease.
    Ⓓ save soldiers who were wounded.

14. Which sentence states a fact?
    Ⓐ Charles was always a good student.
    Ⓑ Charles was always good in sports.
    Ⓒ Charles excelled in track and football.
    Ⓓ Charles's sister died of tuberculosis.

15. Which sentence states an opinion?
    Ⓐ Charles decided to become a doctor.
    Ⓑ Charles went to college in Baltimore, Maryland.
    Ⓒ Dr. Drew was a remarkable man.
    Ⓓ The U.S. Postal Service issued a stamp to honor Charles.

16. What did Dr. Drew do just after World War II began?
    Ⓐ He became a doctor.
    Ⓑ He went to McGill University.
    Ⓒ He wrote a paper called "Banked Blood."
    Ⓓ He became the head of the American Red Cross Blood Bank.

Comprehension

Read each passage and answer the questions that follow.

The Lesson

Last fall, a new kid moved to town. His name was Prescott Howard. As if his name weren't formal enough, he also wore a shirt and tie to school every day. When he spoke, he used the kind of language you would use if you were writing a paper for school. He never participated when we played at recess or after school, even though we always invited him to play. He just hung around and watched with his hands in his pockets.

One day after school, Billy, Marta, Jamal, and I were playing ball at the park. Toby, my dog, was tearing back and forth, barking frantically and trying to catch the ball. Pretty soon there was Prescott, sitting on a bench and watching. We ignored him and kept playing. None of us noticed that Toby had disappeared.

Jamal had just scooped up a tough ground ball when we heard brakes squeal. There was a sharp yelp and then the sound of someone driving away fast. I ran toward the street, but when I got there, Prescott was already kneeling by Toby, talking softly to him. Then I saw the most horrible thing. A bone was sticking out of Toby's back leg. I knelt by his head and put out my hand.

"Don't, Betsy," Prescott said sharply. "He won't recognize you right now, and he might bite you. Give me your jacket." Prescott put his hands underneath Toby and slid him onto the jacket. He was so gentle that Toby barely flinched. Prescott flagged down Ms. Ortega, who happened to be driving by, and asked me, "Who's your vet?"

"Dr. Swanson, on Third Street," I said. Prescott opened the car door and asked Ms. Ortega to take us to Third Street.

Toby didn't look good at all. His tongue was hanging out of his mouth and his eyes were glazed. "Will he be okay?" I blurted out.

"Should be," Prescott said calmly, "if your vet is any good." We pulled up in front of Dr. Swanson's office, and Prescott thanked Ms. Ortega. Dr. Swanson rushed Toby into surgery while Prescott and I sat in the waiting room.

"How'd you learn to take care of animals like that?" I asked.

"My mom's a vet," he said. "I used to help her out."

"Well, where's your mom now?"

"She's sick. She had to go to a clinic far away and my dad went with her, so I came to live with my grandmother for a while. Dad grew up in this town."

I didn't know what to say. I felt awkward and awful. Finally I said stupidly, "I guess you ruined your clothes." There was oil from the road on his pants and a bloodstain on his white shirt.

"I know, isn't it great?" Prescott said happily. I stared at him like he was crazy, and finally he sighed and said, "Grams is nice, but she's old-fashioned. She thinks I should wear a shirt and tie to school. Every afternoon we have tea, and dinner is formal, too. She says I don't speak 'correctly.'" He paused, then added, "Dad asked me to do whatever she asked, and I don't want to let him down."

Boy, had I been wrong about this kid! Just then Dr. Swanson came out. "Betsy, Toby will be fine when his leg heals," he said. "Thank your friend here for knowing what to do and getting Toby here before he really went into shock."

I looked at Prescott, who was smiling widely. On the way out I said, "Maybe we could try to explain to your grandmother about clothes, and, uh . . . your name's okay and all, but it's kind of formal."

"My mom calls me Scotty," he said shyly.

"Then come on, Scotty," I said, "we've got to go tell everyone Toby's going to be all right." I clapped him on the shoulder. "And, hey, Scotty, why don't you lose the tie, just for today?"

He pulled off his tie and stuffed it in his pocket. "Race you to your house," he said, and took off. He was actually pretty fast, but he had on dress shoes, so I beat him.

1. Where were the kids at the beginning of this story?
   - Ⓐ in school
   - Ⓑ at the park
   - Ⓒ on the playground
   - Ⓓ at the vet's office

2. According to Betsy, what was Prescott's problem at the beginning?
   - Ⓐ He did not like dogs.
   - Ⓑ He could not run very fast.
   - Ⓒ He never played with the other kids.
   - Ⓓ He was living with his grandmother.

3. What happened just after Prescott came to watch Betsy and her friends play ball?
   Ⓐ Betsy's dog got hit by a car.
   Ⓑ Prescott flagged down Ms. Ortega.
   Ⓒ Betsy and Scotty raced each other to Betsy's house.
   Ⓓ Prescott took off his tie.

4. Which word *best* describes Prescott's manner with animals?
   Ⓐ silly
   Ⓑ timid
   Ⓒ gentle
   Ⓓ rough

5. Prescott flagged down Ms. Ortega because he
   Ⓐ thought Ms. Ortega had hit Toby.
   Ⓑ needed to take Toby to a vet.
   Ⓒ wanted Ms. Ortega to call the police.
   Ⓓ needed a ride home.

6. How was Prescott *different* from the other kids at first?
   Ⓐ He was a better ball player.
   Ⓑ He was much older.
   Ⓒ He was a better student.
   Ⓓ He was more formal.

7. From this experience, Betsy probably learned that
   Ⓐ everybody likes to play baseball.
   Ⓑ dogs should not be allowed in the park.
   Ⓒ she should not judge people so quickly.
   Ⓓ you can't count on anyone but yourself.

From Ostrich to Kiwi

Cassowary, emu, ostrich, kiwi. What are these strange words? They are all names of birds that cannot fly. While these flightless birds are alike in some ways, there are important differences among these odd creatures.

The ostrich is the largest living bird. It may weigh over 300 pounds and stand up to ten feet tall. Its very long neck, small head, and long, thin legs give it an awkward appearance. The ostrich has beautiful, soft plumage, or feathers. It grazes on the African plains. The ostrich can run up to 35 miles an hour. It can also defend itself with its two large, clawed toes.

The Australian emu looks much like an ostrich but is smaller. It weighs about 120 pounds and stands six feet tall. It can run up to 30 miles an hour and is a good swimmer. The plumage of the emu is hairlike, not feathery. Emus defend themselves by kicking.

The Australian cassowary has a bony crest on its head. Like a rooster, it has red folds of skin that hang down through the neck. Cassowaries have rough and thick hair. They can grow up to six feet tall. They are bold fighters with long, sharp claws on their toes. They have even been known to kill people with their strong kicks.

The odd-looking New Zealand kiwi stands only a foot high. It weighs between 3 and 9 pounds. Its wings are so tiny that they are almost invisible. Kiwis have small heads, almost no neck, and very round bodies covered in coarse brown feathers. In truth, kiwis look sort of like hairy footballs!

8. What is the *main* idea of this passage?
   Ⓐ There are several kinds of unusual, flightless birds.
   Ⓑ Ostriches and emus are very similar in appearance.
   Ⓒ The kiwi is the strangest of all flightless birds.
   Ⓓ Birds that can't fly defend themselves by kicking.

9. Which detail supports the idea that the cassowary is a strange bird?
   Ⓐ It has plumage.
   Ⓑ It can run fast.
   Ⓒ It has claws.
   Ⓓ It has a bony crest on its head.

10. This passage suggests that
    Ⓐ ostriches are the prettiest of all birds.
    Ⓑ kiwis are the strangest looking birds.
    Ⓒ cassowaries are the least dangerous birds.
    Ⓓ emus are the most unusual birds.

11. The ostrich looks awkward because it
    Ⓐ is the largest living bird.
    Ⓑ grazes on the plains.
    Ⓒ has long legs and a long neck.
    Ⓓ can run 35 miles an hour.

12. From this passage, you can infer that the *most* dangerous bird is the
    Ⓐ emu.
    Ⓑ ostrich.
    Ⓒ kiwi.
    Ⓓ cassowary.

13. The purpose of this passage is to
    Ⓐ tell an entertaining story about birds.
    Ⓑ explain why some birds cannot fly.
    Ⓒ describe the animals of Australia.
    Ⓓ give information about birds.

14. Which sentence states an opinion?
    Ⓐ Kiwis look sort of like hairy footballs!
    Ⓑ The ostrich can run up to 35 miles an hour.
    Ⓒ Emus defend themselves by kicking.
    Ⓓ The ostrich is the largest living bird.

15. What is the *main* difference between emus and ostriches?
    Ⓐ their size
    Ⓑ their speed
    Ⓒ their awkward appearance
    Ⓓ their way of defending themselves

16. Which sentence states a fact?
    Ⓐ The ostrich has beautiful plumage.
    Ⓑ Emus weigh about 120 pounds.
    Ⓒ Kiwis look like hairy footballs.
    Ⓓ Cassowaries are bold birds.

Comprehension

Read each passage and answer the questions that follow.

Quicksand

When you hear the word *quicksand*, what image comes to mind? You probably picture someone up to the waist in wet sand, screaming for help. In fact, quicksand can be very dangerous. People and animals have sunk into quicksand before and never escaped. However, the more you know about quicksand, the safer you will be.

First, quicksand is really just ordinary sand. It isn't some sort of strange hungry beast. Quicksand forms when water seeps up from underneath a layer of fine sand. The water pushes the grains of sand apart and makes the sand loose. This loose sand will not hold up a heavy weight.

Quicksand usually forms along the banks of rivers, at the seashore, or under slow-moving rivers and streams. It only forms when water flows upward through the sand, not over it. If you are in a place that tends to have quicksand, it's a good idea to carry a large stick. As you walk, poke the ground in front of you to be sure it's firm.

Let's suppose that you happen to step into some quicksand. The best way to deal with it is to stay calm. You may sink, but you won't sink quickly. You will have time to try several ways to get out. First, drop anything you might be carrying that adds weight, such as a backpack. Then try walking out—making slow and steady movements with your legs. If this doesn't work, the best thing to do is lie back and float. It's even easier to float on quicksand than on regular water.

Of course, you will want to call for help. If help is nearby, it's best simply to wait. If help is not nearby, then continue to lie on your back but make slow, rolling movements toward the edge of the quicksand. When you feel solid ground underneath, you can stand up.

Some animals seem to know how to avoid sinking down into quicksand. Mules, for instance, fold their legs underneath them and float on their bellies. Cows, on the other hand, tend to panic and wave their legs around. This doesn't help them escape. So, if you are ever trapped in quicksand, think like a mule, not like a cow.

1. What is the *main* idea of this passage?
   Ⓐ Quicksand isn't really made up of sand.
   Ⓑ Quicksand can be dangerous, but there are ways to escape.
   Ⓒ You should poke the ground in front of you with a stick.
   Ⓓ Animals are able to float on quicksand, but humans always sink.

2. Which detail supports the idea that quicksand can be dangerous?
   Ⓐ Quicksand forms when water seeps up from underneath.
   Ⓑ You will have time to try several ways to get out.
   Ⓒ Animals have fallen into quicksand and never escaped.
   Ⓓ Quicksand is really just ordinary sand.

3. If you get caught in quicksand, what should you do first?
   Ⓐ Wave your arms and legs quickly.
   Ⓑ Drop anything heavy that you are carrying.
   Ⓒ Fold your legs underneath you.
   Ⓓ Poke a stick into the ground in front of you.

4. How is quicksand different from regular sand?
   Ⓐ It is darker.
   Ⓑ It is more dense.
   Ⓒ It is warmer.
   Ⓓ It is looser.

5. Which sentence states an opinion?
   Ⓐ Quicksand forms when water seeps up from underneath a layer of fine sand.
   Ⓑ People and animals have sunk into quicksand before and never escaped.
   Ⓒ Quicksand is a strange hungry beast.
   Ⓓ Quicksand forms along the banks of rivers, at the seashore, or under slow-moving rivers and streams.

6. The author's *main* purpose in this passage is to
   Ⓐ give information about quicksand.
   Ⓑ tell an entertaining story.
   Ⓒ persuade people to avoid quicksand.
   Ⓓ explain how quicksand forms.

7. Why should you drop anything heavy if you are stuck in quicksand?
   Ⓐ The heavy object in the sand might help push you out.
   Ⓑ Carrying more weight on your body will cause you to sink faster.
   Ⓒ You need your arms free to wave them in the air.
   Ⓓ The drop sound might be heard by someone who can help.

8. How is the mule's reaction to quicksand different from a cow's reaction?
   Ⓐ Mules fold their legs and float on their bellies.
   Ⓑ Mules wave their legs around.
   Ⓒ Mules sink immediately.
   Ⓓ Mules panic and splash their legs around.

The Train Track Mystery

"What's this?" wondered Jenna. She held up a piece of track from a child's train set. A gleam from the track had caught Jenna's eye as she waited in the city train station for her aunt and cousins to arrive.

"Jenna, over here!" cried Aunt Carrie. Jenna knew that her four cousins—Brenda, Kelly, Dawn, and Patsy—couldn't be far behind, so she stashed the piece of track in her backpack and headed toward her aunt. "I'll figure this one out later," thought Jenna.

That night, after finishing her homework and making sure her cousins were asleep, Jenna pulled out the piece of track and studied it. She concluded that it must have come from a very old toy train set, and she wondered how it ended up in the city station. Jenna fell asleep holding the piece of track. She dreamed that she was a girl living back in 1920, and although it had been a difficult year for the family, her parents had purchased a train set for her birthday. It was the circus train that she had wanted so badly after seeing it pictured in a catalog.

Jenna woke up early to the racket of her four-year-old cousin Patsy singing "I've Been Working on the Railroad" at the top of her lungs. "So have I," thought Jenna with a smile. She wanted to study the piece of track again and begin solving the mystery, but then she remembered that today was her great-grandfather's 90th birthday. The family was giving him a surprise party, and it was Jenna's job to find him a present. It had to be something he really wanted and didn't already have, but Jenna had spent a week on this task already and still didn't know what to get.

Suddenly, Jenna had an idea. She would find the owner of the toy train, buy the train, and surprise Great-Grandpa with it. Jenna knew that her great-grandfather liked riding on trains and probably had liked playing with them as a kid, too.

Jenna called every toy store and hobby shop she could find in the local phone book. No one had sold an old train set recently, but one woman suggested she call Depot Antiques. The man who answered the phone there said the track sounded like it had come from an old toy train set he had sold a week before to an older man—a Mr. Samuel Porter. Jenna thanked the man and said goodbye. Then she quickly looked up Mr. Porter in the phone book and called him.

Mr. Porter listened carefully to everything Jenna told him and was quite surprised. He had, in fact, bought the antique train set for his grandson, and one piece was missing when he got it home. Yes, he had passed through the city train station on his way home that day, and perhaps he had dropped the piece of track on the floor and not noticed. Would he sell Jenna the train? Yes, but only for one day. The price? A double birthday party for his grandson, Jeremy, and her great-grandfather. It seemed they had both been born on the same day—85 years apart!

When Mr. Porter and Jeremy arrived that afternoon, it was Jenna's turn to be surprised. Jeremy was just as Jenna had pictured him—an adorable and bright-eyed five-year-old. The surprise was that he was sitting in a wheelchair. Jenna introduced Mr. Porter and Jeremy to the rest of her family, and Mr. Porter said, "Please, call me Sam." Jeremy giggled and handed the train set to Jenna, and then everyone helped to put it together as they waited for Great-Grandpa to arrive.

Great-Grandpa was delighted with the party. He was so pleased to see all of his children, grandchildren, and great-grandchildren—all girls. He joked when he saw Jeremy that it was nice to have another male around. Then he spotted the train set, and his eyes lit up. "The Big Circus Train set! The one I wanted as a boy! How did you know? Where did you find it?"

Jenna explained how she'd found the piece of track and how it had led her to Jeremy and his grandfather. Great-Grandpa seemed to like the story almost as much as the train set. "I love a good mystery," he commented. "You would make an excellent detective, Jenna."

All afternoon, Jeremy sat right next to Great-Grandpa, and the two of them took turns making the sound of a train whistle. All the kids, big and small, took turns running the train. Jenna had indeed gotten Great-Grandpa something he didn't already have and really wanted—a chance to be a kid again and play with the train set of his dreams.

9. Which sentence states a fact?
   Ⓐ Great-Grandpa was delighted with the party.
   Ⓑ "You would make an excellent detective, Jenna."
   Ⓒ She concluded that it must have come from a very old set train set.
   Ⓓ Jeremy and her great-grandfather were born on the very same day—85 years apart.

10. What was Jenna's problem?
    Ⓐ She had to meet Jeremy.
    Ⓑ She needed to find a good birthday present for her great-grandfather.
    Ⓒ She could not find her answers.
    Ⓓ She got lost on her way to the train station.

11. What question was Jenna trying to answer?
    Ⓐ Who is Jeremy?
    Ⓑ Where is the train set that is missing a piece?
    Ⓒ Why did she dream about being a girl in 1920?
    Ⓓ When will Aunt Carrie and her cousins visit again?

12. Which of these events happened first?
    Ⓐ Jenna dreamed about a train set.
    Ⓑ Jenna did her homework.
    Ⓒ Jenna met her aunt at the train station.
    Ⓓ Jenna pulled out the piece of track.

13. Jenna woke up early in the morning because
    Ⓐ her cousin was singing.
    Ⓑ the phone rang.
    Ⓒ a train whistled.
    Ⓓ Great-Grandpa called her.

14. The author's *main* purpose in this passage is to
    Ⓐ show how the main character solves a mystery.
    Ⓑ share information about different train sets.
    Ⓒ tell about Jenna's special birthday party.
    Ⓓ share a story about how Great-Grandpa and Jeremy met.

15. Why do you think Jenna dreamed of living as a girl in the 1920s?
    Ⓐ She was thinking about her Great-Grandpa's life in 1920s.
    Ⓑ She fell asleep holding a piece of a very old train set.
    Ⓒ She had just read a book about the 1920s.
    Ⓓ She had just learned about the 1920s era in school.

16. Which word *best* describes Mr. Porter?
    Ⓐ kind
    Ⓑ nervous
    Ⓒ strict
    Ⓓ rude

Collins for President

My fellow classmates, my name is Jerry Collins. I'm standing beneath our school safety patrol award, announcing my candidacy for a very important office. Today I am asking you to join the large number of intelligent people backing me for class president. I have letters from Lynn Tokubo, this year's science award winner, Betsy Collins, last year's track-and-field medal winner, and Pete Anders, winner of this year's sports medal, saying they will vote for me. I also have the support of several of my classmates, saying that they will vote for me. Each of these people knows that I can be counted on to represent our class. Each knows that I am the very best person for the job!

But why should you vote for me? What will I bring to this role that the other candidates lack? I have a proven record of success in school government. Last year, I served as a member of our student council, working closely with class president Andy Burke. Together with Andy and other dedicated student council members, I worked on several important projects for the benefit of our school. Based on this and many other experiences, I know what our school needs, and I know how to convince others to help us reach our goals.

I also have the personal skills needed to succeed as class president! I am sympathetic to the needs of all students. I am good at organizing things, I work hard, and I am unselfish. I am a loyal patriot of our school. I am diplomatic and therefore know how to get along with all kinds of people. Most important of all, I know how to get a tough job accomplished. Don't be fooled into a vote you will be sorry for later on. We need a better student government. And we need it now. Vote for the best person for the job. Vote for Jerry Collins for class president!

1. The Greek root word *path* means "feeling" or "suffering." Someone who is sympathetic
   Ⓐ is very emotional.
   Ⓑ tries to understand how others feel.
   Ⓒ is friendly and outgoing.
   Ⓓ knows how to get a tough job accomplished.

2. Which words are in the *same* word family as patriot?
   Ⓐ patriotic, patriotism
   Ⓑ pattern, patty
   Ⓒ patch, patchwork
   Ⓓ soldier, country

3. "What will I bring to this role that the other candidates lack?" In this sentence, an *antonym* for lack is
   Ⓐ possess.
   Ⓑ need.
   Ⓒ want.
   Ⓓ miss.

4. Which of the following does the candidate do throughout the speech?
   Ⓐ makes obviously true statements
   Ⓑ makes only favorable comments about himself
   Ⓒ provides enough facts to back up his statements
   Ⓓ tells specific faults of the present student government

5. What is this speech trying to get the listeners to do?
   Ⓐ vote for a candidate
   Ⓑ earn a science award
   Ⓒ promote school safety
   Ⓓ run for class president

6. Summarize this candidate's argument for why he should be class president. Use details from the passage to support your answer.

____

____

____

____

Easter Island

Jacob Roggeveen was in for a big surprise. The Dutch explorer had landed on a small, barren island in a remote part of the South Pacific. It was Easter Sunday in 1722, so he named this exotic place Easter Island. He really did not expect to find much because the island was so far from any other land. But to his astonishment, he found hundreds of giant stone heads. Some of the heads were standing, but many had fallen and collapsed.

The Dutch sailors thought the heads were constructed of clay, but they were actually carved from volcanic rock. No written history exists to explain these giant statues. They have puzzled explorers and scientists ever since Europeans first came to Easter Island. Who made the statues and why? How could they carve the heads? How could they move them?

Almost 900 heads, called *moai* (*MOH eye*), have been found. Most archeologists believe the heads represent the spirits of ancestors or chiefs. Many of the heads stand on the coast, with their backs to the ocean. Nearly half of the heads never made it out of the quarry. The largest head is almost 72 feet tall and weighs about 150 tons. The smallest is about 4 feet tall. The average height is about 13 feet.

The people of Easter Island have an interesting history. Easter Island is very isolated, as it is almost 2,500 miles east of South America. Tahiti is 2,500 miles to the west, and the nearest land is tiny Pitcairn Island, 1,400 miles away. The island's soil is stony, and the only fresh water comes from wells and lakes in three extinct volcanoes.

Most scientists now agree that Polynesians came to Easter Island by canoe between A.D. 400 and 700. The settlers found large forests of palm trees, and planted the banana trees and taro root they brought with them for food. They cleared the forests to plant their crops, and used the wood to build houses and shrines. However, without a forest cover, the thin topsoil eroded rapidly, and soon the islanders found that the land had become less productive.

As the settlers began to carve the giant statues, they cut down more trees to make rollers to move the huge heads. Soon, wood became so scarce that the islanders could no longer build canoes. Without canoes, they could not fish out in the ocean. Even worse, they could not leave—they were trapped on the island.

With fewer resources, the island could not support its population. War broke out between rival groups, villages were plundered and destroyed, and statues were pushed over and broken. The situation rapidly became worse after the Europeans came. American whaling ships kidnapped people when they needed extra crew members, and in the 1860s, slave-traders from Peru took captives to sell. At least a third of the population—more than 1,400 people—was sold into slavery.

Eventually, the government of Peru decided to send the captives home. About 470 islanders were put on a ship, but only 100 made it back alive. The survivors brought the disease smallpox with them, which nearly killed all of the people living on the island. By the early 1900s, only about 100 people remained.

Easter Island became a colony of Chile in 1888. Mostly it was used as a giant sheep ranch, and at one point, there were over 70,000 sheep on the island. The sheep further destroyed the island's vegetation. The sheep ranchers also planted non-native trees that used up scarce water supplies. The ranchers treated the islanders poorly, until finally, the islanders revolted. Many others tried to escape.

Regular airline service to Easter Island finally began in 1967. By the 1970s, the islanders developed a running water system and had electricity. The population is now up to 2,000. Hotels were built for tourists. Television, telephones, and Internet service are available. Tourism is a big business on the island, but it is a mixed blessing. Although only about 5,000 visitors came in 1990, over 21,000 came in 1999. Now there are efforts to protect both the fragile land and the amazing stone heads.

7. What is the *main* idea of the last paragraph of the passage?
   Ⓐ The number of tourists has increased from 5,000 to 21,000.
   Ⓑ The Easter Islanders now have telephones, television, and Internet service.
   Ⓒ Tourism is important, but the island needs to be protected.
   Ⓓ Many people want to come see the giant heads.

8. Which of the following was *not* an effect of cutting down the trees?
   Ⓐ The people were trapped on Easter Island.
   Ⓑ The islanders could not go fishing in the open ocean.
   Ⓒ The topsoil eroded and the land became less productive.
   Ⓓ The sheep further destroyed the island's vegetation.

9. Which generalization applies to *all* of the giant statues on Easter Island?
   Ⓐ Most can be found on the coast.
   Ⓑ Most are very large, averaging 13 feet tall.
   Ⓒ Most are still in the quarry.
   Ⓓ Most have been found.

10. Which of the following statements is an opinion?
   Ⓐ The statues were pushed over and the villages were destroyed.
   Ⓑ The island's population was almost destroyed by smallpox.
   Ⓒ The islanders should not have fought over their scarce resources.
   Ⓓ The islanders needed canoes so that they could fish in the ocean.

11. From the passage, you can probably conclude that life on the island
    Ⓐ became increasingly difficult after all the trees were cut down.
    Ⓑ was impossible because the people could not grow enough food.
    Ⓒ got better after Easter Island became a colony of Chile.
    Ⓓ was so easy that the people could spend a lot of time carving statues.

12. According to the passage, which of these events happened between the arrival of slave traders from Peru and the introduction of 70,000 sheep to the island?
    Ⓐ Easter Island became a colony of Chile.
    Ⓑ The warring groups broke statues and destroyed villages.
    Ⓒ American whaling ships captured people from the island.
    Ⓓ The islanders revolted and tried to escape.

13. What is the author's purpose in writing this passage?

    ____

    ____

14. Explain two effects of cutting down the trees on Easter Island. Use details from the passage to support your response.

    ____

    ____

    ____

    ____

Pandora's Box

Zeus was furious, and everyone on Mount Olympus knew it. All the other gods and goddesses were tiptoeing around, terrified of his temper. Life on Olympus was miserable whenever Zeus was mad.

He simply could not understand how this ridiculous situation had occurred. He was Zeus, lord of lightning and thunder! He alone could make the mountains shake and the fire crackle and rage—that is, until now. He had been tricked! That devious Prometheus and his brother had stolen fire and given it to the humans.

Zeus summoned Hermes the messenger, saying, "I want to send Prometheus a present, Hermes, just to show him there are no hard feelings." Hermes's eyebrows shot up, but he knew better than to say anything. Then Zeus brought forth the most beautiful woman anyone had ever seen. "Her name is Pandora," Zeus said, "my gift to Prometheus."

Sometime later, weary Hermes set his burden down on Prometheus's doorstep. When Prometheus learned that Pandora was a gift from Zeus, he was immediately suspicious. He turned to Hermes to refuse the gift, but he was too late. Hermes was already gone.

Prometheus's brother, Epimetheus, was not as skeptical as Prometheus. Immediately, Epimetheus asked Pandora to marry him. They settled down to a happy life together. Before too long, however, Hermes appeared at their door, grinning broadly and holding out a magnificent package. "I have a wedding present for Pandora and Epimetheus!" he called. "Special delivery from Zeus himself!"

Pandora accepted the package graciously and started to untie the ribbons. "Be patient, Pandora," Hermes warned. "Zeus would like to be here when you open his present. Please be so kind as to wait for his arrival." Of course, Pandora agreed.

Pandora waited and waited, but Zeus never came. The longer she waited, the more curious she became about the present. What could it be? After all, the gift was from the king of the gods himself, so it must be gold—or silver, or diamonds, or emeralds. Why shouldn't she take a little peek inside? She could rewrap it and no one would know. She argued with Epimetheus to open the box just once. Epimetheus, however, wanted no more trouble with Zeus, and he warned her to be patient.

One morning, after Epimetheus left to go hunting, Pandora finally gave in to temptation. Gently, carefully, she untied the intricate knots and smoothed out the exquisite ribbons. Her heart thumping anxiously, she raised the lid, anticipating the sparkle of gems or the gleam of gold.

Then, to her horror, out of the box flew plague after plague—War! Disease! Famine! Drought! They were spilling from the gift, buzzing around her head like insects. Too late she realized that Zeus had packed the box with all of the pain and suffering and evil he could imagine.

Realizing her dreadful mistake, Pandora swatted at the plagues, desperately trying to shove them back into the box. She slammed the lid, but it was too late. She buried her head in her arms, weeping bitterly and pounding on the box. Oh, she was so sorry now—sorry for her curiosity, sorry for her impatience, and sorry for all the misery and sorrow she had let loose into the world.

After she had sobbed her heart out and had no more tears to cry, she laid her head on the box, exhausted. Then she heard a little voice, faint and faraway. "Let me out!" the voice twittered, barely audible. "Please let me out!" She flattened her ear against the top of the box and listened closely.

"Please, please, pleeeeease," pleaded the tiny voice.

"Oh, what's the difference anyway," moaned Pandora. "You surely can't be any worse than all the other evil things." Just in case, she raised the lid ever so slowly.

Out fluttered a graceful butterfly. It swooped and floated into every corner of the room. Finally, it landed on Pandora's shoulder and folded its splendid wings.

"I thought you'd never hear me," it whispered. "My name is Hope."

1. Who is telling this story?
   Ⓐ Zeus
   Ⓑ Pandora
   Ⓒ Hermes
   Ⓓ the narrator

2. Which statement *best* describes the difference between Prometheus and Epithemeus?
   Ⓐ Zeus is angrier with Prometheus than he is with Epithemeus.
   Ⓑ Epithemeus is less worried than Prometheus about Zeus's intentions.
   Ⓒ Epithemeus trusts Pandora less than Prometheus does.
   Ⓓ Prometheus feels more guilty than Epithemeus for stealing fire.

3. Why does Pandora open the present even though she has been asked to wait?
   Ⓐ She does not think she should have to wait for Zeus to arrive.
   Ⓑ She is angry with Epithemeus because she does not want to share the present.
   Ⓒ She is angry about getting a present from the king of the gods.
   Ⓓ She is curious about the present and excited about what might be inside.

4. What happens immediately after Pandora opens the box?
   Ⓐ She tries to find Epithemeus to help her close the box.
   Ⓑ She tries to shove the plagues back into the box.
   Ⓒ She pleads with Zeus to take back all of the evil.
   Ⓓ She releases the butterfly named Hope.

5. In one or two sentences, describe the theme of this story.

   ____

   ____

6. Describe an example of foreshadowing in the story. In your response, be sure to describe the event or events that are being foreshadowed.

   ____

   ____

   ____

   ____

   ____

Deena's Toughest Audience

Deena finished the last chord of the piano composition. She was just as nervous now as if she were playing in front of an audience. "If I'm this nervous at the recital Sunday," she thought, "I'll automatically make a mistake!" Trying to ignore this discouragement, Deena turned back to the piano to play the piece once more.

Suddenly, alerted by the pleasant chirping of Chester, her parakeet, she stopped. Chester stopped. She played another measure. Chester tilted his bluish head and chirped right along in obvious enjoyment. Then Deena played the first few measures of a gypsy song she had not yet learned to play perfectly. She bumbled through some of the difficult parts, and she hit some wrong notes. Chester squawked wildly and jumped up and down on his perch.

As soon as Deena changed back to the piece she knew well, Chester calmed down, chirping softly and contentedly. "Chester, my favorite critic, you deserve an extra Budgie Treat," Deena cried as she confidently returned to her practicing. All afternoon, Deena played the new piece over and over again, concentrating hard on the difficult parts. The whole time, she listened for Chester's approval or disapproval, depending on his chirp. She thought, "I don't have to worry about other audiences. I've been prepared by my toughest audience right here at home!"

The next day, Deena's recital was a huge success and quite an accomplishment. She played all her pieces confidently, including the new, complex piece she had practiced so hard the day before. After she stood and took her bow, her piano teacher came onto the stage to congratulate her. "What a wonderful surprise that was, Deena!" Mrs. Wagner began. "You've only had the music for that gypsy song for a few weeks, and yet you played it perfectly!"

"Well," Deena responded, "I *have* been practicing really hard, but I also had extra help when I was working on the difficult parts." Noticing the puzzled look on Mrs. Wagner's face, Deena laughed. "Oh, don't worry, Mrs. Wagner. I don't have a new teacher—just a very special little friend!"

7. This story is written from the point of view of
   Ⓐ the parakeet.
   Ⓑ Deena.
   Ⓒ a first person narrator.
   Ⓓ a third person narrator.

8. Which of the following things did *not* help Deena perform well at her recital?
   Ⓐ She practiced the music and was prepared to play it.
   Ⓑ Her bird showed her where she needed to improve.
   Ⓒ She gained confidence from knowing the music well.
   Ⓓ She took extra lessons with another music teacher.

9. When and where does most of this story take place?
   Ⓐ on the stage at the recital on Sunday
   Ⓑ in Deena's house on Saturday
   Ⓒ on the stage on Saturday and Sunday
   Ⓓ at Mrs. Wagner's piano studio

10. Briefly describe a possible theme in this story.

____

____

____

____

____

The Birth of the Motion Picture

On a cold December day in 1895, people excitedly lined up outside a café in Paris, France. When the doors opened, they bought their tickets and took their seats. They saw a twenty-minute program of ten short films, including a movie of workers leaving a factory. They saw a man riding a bicycle and a horse-drawn carriage galloping across the screen. They laughed at a film showing a gardener getting soaked by his own hose. They cheered as a locomotive steamed into a railroad station.

Most of these films were about boring, everyday subjects, yet the audience was amazed by the whole program. These were the first movies shown on a screen in a theater, and people found them fascinating. That date, December 28, 1895, is considered the official birthday of the movies.

The show was put on by two French brothers, Louis and Auguste Lumière. Today, they are considered the "founding fathers of film," but they did not think the movies would last. They did not think people would pay attention to images on a screen for hours. If they could foresee the future, they would know how wrong they were!

The Lumières were not the first inventors to think about capturing movement on film. Many other scientists and inventors had already solved parts of the problem. Scientists knew that still images, when set in motion, gave the illusion of movement. Optical toys, such as "flipbooks," were becoming increasingly common. A flipbook has slightly different drawings on each page. When the user flips the pages rapidly, the images seem to move.

Another popular toy was the zoetrope. This hollow spinning cylinder had slits on the outside and different pictures on the inside. When the user spins the cylinder and looks through a slit, the images seem to move. Until the beginning of photography in the 1830s, all the images were drawings.

In the 1870s, an early British photographer named Eadweard Muybridge made a breakthrough. He wanted to prove that, when a horse is galloping, all four hooves are off the ground at once. He set up twelve cameras and tripwires along a racetrack, and as the horse ran, it tripped the wires and the cameras took the pictures. These were the first successful photographs of motion.

The famous American inventor of the phonograph, Thomas Edison, became interested in motion pictures in the 1880s. Edison asked an employee, William K.L. Dickson, to make two machines: one was for recording movement on film and one was for looking at the images.

Dickson made a motion-picture camera that took pictures on long strips of film, with holes along the sides of the film to hold it in place. A motor advanced the film one frame at a time. The camera was a huge step forward.

The viewing machine, called the Kinetoscope, was a tall box that stood on the floor. The user put in money and looked down into the box to watch the movie. Only one person could use the machine at a time. Edison built the first motion-picture studio to make films for the Kinetoscope. His studio was just a small shack that he covered in black tarpaper.

Soon, Kinetoscope "parlors" opened up. These rooms were filled with rows of the machines, like today's video game arcades. The films were only 30 to 60 seconds long. Most were about everyday subjects, like someone's home movies. One was a film of a man sneezing. In 1894, nearly 500 people paid twenty-five cents to see Edison's movies.

The Lumière brothers' innovation was a combination camera and projector. It was portable and lightweight, and could be connected to a projector to show large images on a screen. Their method was also a more profitable way of showing films, because more than one person could watch at a time. Edison and others quickly took advantage of the idea.

Changes and improvements came rapidly. Films became longer, up to 15 minutes, and movie theaters opened. Moviemakers learned to edit the film and developed other techniques. They started telling stories and filming important events as they happened. One thing was still missing, however. Almost thirty years passed before the next big breakthrough—adding sound to the images—in 1927.

11. Which of the following generalizations could you make about the invention of motion pictures?
    Ⓐ Thomas Edison did not have much to do with the invention of motion pictures.
    Ⓑ French inventors were more advanced than British or American inventors.
    Ⓒ Motion pictures were the result of different inventions and advancements over a long time.
    Ⓓ Motion pictures did not become popular until sound was added to the films.

12. Why was the audience at the café in 1895 so excited?
    Ⓐ They liked to laugh at funny films and to be frightened by scary ones.
    Ⓑ They probably knew all the people in the films they saw.
    Ⓒ They were the first people to see motion pictures on a big screen.
    Ⓓ They had never before seen ten films all at the same time.

13. Which problem was *not* solved by the Lumière brothers' innovations?
    Ⓐ Early movie cameras were heavy and hard to move from place to place.
    Ⓑ Early movies had to be seen on separate viewing machines called Kinetoscopes.
    Ⓒ Early movies had no soundtrack on the film.
    Ⓓ Early movies could only be seen by one person at a time.

14. Which of the following is an opinion?
    Ⓐ Most of the early films were about boring subjects.
    Ⓑ Flipbooks have slightly different drawings on every page.
    Ⓒ The Lumière brothers invented a combination of a camera and a projector.
    Ⓓ Nearly 500 people paid money to look at Edison's movies on the viewing machines.

15. The author believes that the Lumière brothers are the "founding fathers" of the movies because
    Ⓐ their inventions were more important than Dickson's camera and viewing machine.
    Ⓑ their films were projected on large screens in theaters, as movies are today.
    Ⓒ they showed that people would pay attention to images on a screen for hours.
    Ⓓ their movies really amazed and excited the people who came to see them.

16. How were the inventions of Dickson and the Lumière brothers similar? How were they different?

____

____

____

____

____

Answer Key

KINDERGARTEN

1. 1st picture
2. 2nd picture
3. 3rd picture
4. 1st picture
5. 1st picture
6. 2nd picture

GRADE 1

1. C 2. B 3. A 4. C
5. C 6. A 7. A 8. A

GRADE 2

1. D 2. A 3. D 4. A
5. B 6. C 7. A 8. B
9. B 10. D

GRADE 3

1. D 2. A 3. B 4. A
5. B 6. B 7. A 8. C
9. D 10. B

GRADE 4

1. C 2. A 3. D 4. C
5. A 6. B 7. C 8. B
9. C 10. D 11. B 12. C
13. A 14. D 15. C 16. D

GRADE 5

1. B 2. C 3. A 4. C
5. B 6. D 7. C 8. A
9. D 10. B 11. C 12. D
13. D 14. A 15. A 16. B

GRADE 6

1. B 2. C 3. B 4. D
5. C 6. A 7. B 8. A
9. D 10. B 11. B 12. C
13. A 14. A 15. B 16. A

GRADE 7

1. B 2. A 3. A 4. C
5. A 6. Summary should include only the most important facts.
7. C 8. D 9. B 10. C
11. A 12. A
13. Answers will vary, but should be supported.
14. Answers will vary, but should be supported.

GRADE 8

1. D 2. B 3. D 4. B
5. Answers will vary, but may include something about patience or hope.
6. Possible answers include Hermes raising his eyebrows, Hermes leaving before the gift was opened, or Hermes telling Pandora to wait to open the box.
7. D 8. D 9. B
10. Answers will vary, but may include something about hard work, practice, or building confidence.
11. C 12. C 13. C 14. A
15. B
16 Answers will vary, but should include facts from the article.

Scoring Chart

The Scoring Chart is provided for your convenience in grading your students' work.

- Find the column that shows the total number of items on the test.
- Find the row that matches the number of items answered correctly.
- The intersection of the column and the row provides the percentage score.

NUMBER CORRECT	TOTAL NUMBER OF ITEMS										
	6	7	8	9	10	11	12	13	14	15	16
1	17	14	13	11	10	9	8	8	7	7	6
2	33	29	25	22	20	18	17	15	14	13	13
3	50	43	38	33	30	27	25	23	21	20	19
4	67	57	50	44	40	36	33	31	29	27	25
5	83	71	63	56	50	45	42	38	36	33	31
6	100	86	75	67	60	55	50	46	46	40	38
7		100	88	78	70	64	58	54	50	47	44
8			100	89	80	73	67	62	57	53	50
9				100	90	82	75	69	64	60	56
10					100	91	83	77	71	67	63
11						100	92	85	79	73	69
12							100	95	86	80	75
13								100	93	87	81
14									100	93	88
15										100	94
16											100

Metacomprehension Strategy Index Grades K-8

▶ **WHAT** The *Metacomprehension Strategy Index* (developed by Schmitt, 1988, 1990) assesses students' independent use of strategies before, during, and after reading. Students read a series of questions about their reading behaviors. Questions cover broad areas such as predicting and verifying, previewing, purpose setting, self-questioning, drawing from background knowledge, summarizing, and using appropriate fix-up strategies.

Predicting and Verifying: Items numbered 1, 4, 13, 15, 16, 18, 23

Predicting the content of a story promotes active comprehension by giving readers a purpose for reading. Evaluating predictions and generating new ones as necessary enhances the constructive nature of the reading process.

Previewing: Items numbered 2, 3

Previewing the text facilitates comprehension by activating background knowledge and providing information for making predictions.

Purpose Setting: Items numbered 5, 7, 21

Reading with a purpose promotes active, strategic reading.

Self-Questioning: Items numbered 6, 14, 17

Generating questions to be answered promotes active comprehension by giving readers a purpose for reading.

Drawing from Background Knowledge: Items numbered 8, 9, 10, 19, 24, 25

Activating and incorporating information from background knowledge contributes to comprehension by helping readers make inferences and generate predictions.

Summarizing and Applying Fix-Up Strategies: Items numbered 11, 12, 20, 22

Summarizing the content at various points in the story serves as a form of comprehension monitoring. Rereading when comprehension breaks down represents strategic reading.
(from *Metacognition in Literacy Learning;* S. Israel, C. C. Block, K. Bauserman, K. Kinnucan-Welsch, 2005, page 105)

▶ WHY Comprehension is the ultimate goal of reading. Developing skilled, independent, strategic readers is the goal of comprehension instruction. This assessment helps you determine if students are using strategies before, during, and after reading and which ones they might be using. The assessment can provide insights into each student's strategic processing of text and affect the amount and types of strategy instruction you provide to students.

▶ HOW Make booklets for students by copying the series of questions. Distribute the booklets to the students.

Explain to students that this test will help you determine the strategies they use while reading so you can help them become more skilled and strategic readers. Make sure students are sitting in a comfortable setting with minimal distractions, and encourage them to do their best on the test.

In order to administer the test efficiently and make the directions understandable, you should be familiar with the directions and the test items before the test is given. During the administration, monitor students closely to make sure that each student is following the directions, is on the correct item, and is marking the test form correctly.

▶ WHAT IT MEANS This assessment can be scored using the Answer Key at the end of this section (page 70). It lists the correct response for each question. Mark each incorrect item on the student's test and record the number of correct items by category: Before Reading, During Reading, After Reading. In addition, use the item analysis information on pages 62–63 to determine which types of strategies students are not using (e.g., summarizing and fix-up strategies as indicated by items 11, 12, 20, and 22).

Use the results of the assessment to form small groups based on strategy needs. Provide additional instruction on these strategies during small-group time, and help students apply the strategies using the Skills-Based Practice Readers. In addition, reinforce those strategies not mastered during whole-group reading sessions in which students are asked to explain their self-selected strategy use.

METACOMPREHENSION STRATEGY INDEX

Directions: Think about what kinds of things you can do to understand a story better before, during, and after you read it. Read each of the lists of four statements and decide which one of them would help *you* the most. *There are no right answers*. It is just what *you* think would help the most. Circle the letter of the statement you choose.

I. In each set of four, choose the one statement which tells a good thing to do to help you understand a story better *before* you read it.

1. Before I begin reading, it's a good idea to
   Ⓐ see how many pages are in the story.
   Ⓑ look up all of the big words in the dictionary.
   Ⓒ make some guesses about what I think will happen in the story.
   Ⓓ think about what has happened so far in the story.

2. Before I begin reading, it's a good idea to
   Ⓐ look at the pictures to see what the story is about.
   Ⓑ decide how long it will take me to read the story.
   Ⓒ sound out the words I don't know.
   Ⓓ check to see if the story is making sense.

3. Before I begin reading, it's a good idea to
   Ⓐ ask someone to read the story to me.
   Ⓑ read the title to see what the story is about.
   Ⓒ check to see if most of the words have long or short vowels in them.
   Ⓓ check to see if the pictures are in order and make sense.

4. Before I begin reading, it's a good idea to
   Ⓐ check to see that no pages are missing.
   Ⓑ make a list of words I'm not sure about.
   Ⓒ use the title and pictures to help me make guesses about what will happen in the story.
   Ⓓ read the last sentence so I will know how the story ends.

METACOMPREHENSION STRATEGY INDEX (continued)

5. Before I begin reading, it's a good idea to
   Ⓐ decide on why I am going to read the story.
   Ⓑ use the difficult words to help me make guesses about what will happen in the story.
   Ⓒ reread some parts to see if I can figure out what is happening if things aren't making sense.
   Ⓓ ask for help with the difficult words.

6. Before I begin reading, it's a good idea to
   Ⓐ retell all of the main points that have happened so far.
   Ⓑ ask myself questions that I would like to have answered in the story.
   Ⓒ think about the meanings of the words which have more than one meaning.
   Ⓓ look through the story to find all of the words with three or more syllables.

7. Before I begin reading, it's a good idea to
   Ⓐ check to see if I have read this story before.
   Ⓑ use my questions and guesses as a reason for reading the story.
   Ⓒ make sure I can pronounce all of the words before I start.
   Ⓓ think of a better title for the story.

8. Before I begin reading, it's a good idea to
   Ⓐ think of what I already know about the things I see in the pictures.
   Ⓑ see how many pages are in the story.
   Ⓒ choose the best part of the story to read again.
   Ⓓ read the story aloud to someone.

9. Before I begin reading, it's a good idea to
   Ⓐ practice reading the story aloud.
   Ⓑ retell all of the main points to make sure I can remember the story.
   Ⓒ think of what the people in the story might be like.
   Ⓓ decide if I have enough time to read the story.

METACOMPREHENSION STRATEGY INDEX (continued)

10. Before I begin reading, it's a good idea to
    - Ⓐ check to see if I am understanding the story so far.
    - Ⓑ check to see if the words have more than one meaning.
    - Ⓒ think about where the story might be taking place.
    - Ⓓ list all of the important details.

II. In each set of four, choose the one statement which tells a good thing to do to help you understand a story better *while* you are reading it.

11. While I'm reading, it's a good idea to
    - Ⓐ read the story very slowly so that I will not miss any important parts.
    - Ⓑ read the title to see what the story is about.
    - Ⓒ check to see if the pictures have anything missing.
    - Ⓓ check to see if the story is making sense by seeing if I can tell what's happened so far.

12. While I'm reading, it's a good idea to
    - Ⓐ stop to retell the main points to see if I am understanding what has happened so far.
    - Ⓑ read the story quickly so that I can find out what happened.
    - Ⓒ read only the beginning and the end of the story to find out what it is about.
    - Ⓓ skip the parts that are too difficult for me.

13. While I'm reading, it's a good idea to
    - Ⓐ look all of the big words up in the dictionary.
    - Ⓑ put the book away and find another one if things aren't making sense.
    - Ⓒ keep thinking about the title and the pictures to help me decide what is going to happen next.
    - Ⓓ keep track of how many pages I have left to read.

METACOMPREHENSION STRATEGY INDEX (continued)

14. While I'm reading, it's a good idea to
    Ⓐ keep track of how long it is taking me to read the story.
    Ⓑ check to see if I can answer any of the questions I asked before I started reading.
    Ⓒ read the title to see what the story is going to be about.
    Ⓓ add the missing details to the pictures.

15. While I'm reading, it's a good idea to
    Ⓐ have someone read the story aloud to me.
    Ⓑ keep track of how many pages I have read.
    Ⓒ list the story's main character.
    Ⓓ check to see if my guesses are right or wrong.

16. While I'm reading, it's a good idea to
    Ⓐ check to see that the characters are real.
    Ⓑ make a lot of guesses about what is going to happen next.
    Ⓒ not look at the pictures because they might confuse me.
    Ⓓ read the story aloud to someone.

17. While I'm reading, it's a good idea to
    Ⓐ try to answer the questions I asked myself.
    Ⓑ try not to confuse what I already know with what I'm reading about.
    Ⓒ read the story silently.
    Ⓓ check to see if I am saying the new vocabulary words correctly.

18. While I'm reading, it's a good idea to
    Ⓐ try to see if my guesses are going to be right or wrong.
    Ⓑ reread to be sure I haven't missed any of the words.
    Ⓒ decide on why I am reading the story.
    Ⓓ list what happened first, second, third, and so on.

METACOMPREHENSION STRATEGY INDEX (continued)

19. While I'm reading, it's a good idea to
   Ⓐ see if I can recognize the new vocabulary words.
   Ⓑ be careful not to skip any parts of the story.
   Ⓒ check to see how many of the words I already know.
   Ⓓ keep thinking of what I already know about the things and ideas in the story to help me decide what is going to happen.

20. While I'm reading, it's a good idea to
   Ⓐ reread some parts or read ahead to see if I can figure out what is happening if things aren't making sense.
   Ⓑ take my time reading so that I can be sure I understand what is happening.
   Ⓒ change the ending so that it makes sense.
   Ⓓ check to see if there are enough pictures to help make the story ideas clear.

III. In each set of four, choose the one statement which tells a good thing to do to help you understand a story better *after* you have read it.

21. After I've read a story, it's a good idea to
   Ⓐ count how many pages I read with no mistakes.
   Ⓑ check to see if there were enough pictures to go with the story to make it interesting.
   Ⓒ check to see if I met my purpose for reading the story.
   Ⓓ underline the causes and effects.

22. After I've read a story, it's a good idea to
   Ⓐ underline the main idea.
   Ⓑ retell the main points of the whole story so that I can check to see if I understood it.
   Ⓒ read the story again to be sure I said all of the words right.
   Ⓓ practice reading the story aloud.

METACOMPREHENSION STRATEGY INDEX (continued)

23. After I've read a story, it's a good idea to
    - Ⓐ read the title and look over the story to see what it is about.
    - Ⓑ check to see if I skipped any of the vocabulary words.
    - Ⓒ think about what made me make good or bad predictions.
    - Ⓓ make a guess about what will happen next in the story.

24. After I've read a story, it's a good idea to
    - Ⓐ look up all of the big words in the dictionary.
    - Ⓑ read the best parts aloud.
    - Ⓒ have someone read the story aloud to me.
    - Ⓓ think about how the story was like things I already knew about before I started reading.

25. After I've read a story, it's a good idea to
    - Ⓐ think about how I would have acted if I were the main character in the story.
    - Ⓑ practice reading the story silently for practice of good reading.
    - Ⓒ look over the story title and pictures to see what will happen.
    - Ⓓ make a list of the things I understood the most.

METACOMPREHENSION STRATEGY INDEX (continued)

DIRECTIONS FOR SCORING

Part One: Responses that indicate metacomprehension strategy awareness.

I. Before Reading:	II. During Reading:	III. After Reading:
1. C	11. D	21. C
2. A	12. A	22. B
3. B	13. C	23. C
4. C	14. B	24. D
5. A	15. D	25. A
6. B	16. B	
7. B	17. A	
8. A	18. A	
9. C	19. D	
10. C	20. A	

McLeod Assessment of Reading Comprehension

▶ **WHAT** The *McLeod Assessment of Reading Comprehension* assesses reading comprehension by means of the "cloze" technique, in which students read a series of passages and supply words that have been deleted from sentences within each passage. Supplying the correct word requires comprehension of the sentences within the passage. While the passages are ordered in respect to difficulty, individual passages do not represent a specific grade level like those that appear in the *Fry Oral Reading Test*. Interpretation is based on the total number of correct words supplied for all passages administered. Two levels of the test assess reading comprehension in grades 2–5 and in grades 6–8 and above.

▶ **WHY** Comprehension is the ultimate goal of reading. This assessment requires students to accurately decode words, to apply their knowledge of grammar, syntax, and vocabulary, and to use critical reading strategies that aid in the literal and inferential comprehension of what is read. When administered to everyone in a class, the *McLeod Assessment of Reading Comprehension* serves as a valuable screening tool for identifying students who may have reading difficulties and who may benefit from additional assessment that focuses on specific skills underlying reading. It is useful to test frequently in the elementary and middle school grades.

▶ **HOW** Make booklets for students by copying either the elementary or upper level test pages that follow. For the youngest students, you may want to use only the first two to four passages of the elementary level. Distribute the booklets to the students.

SAY: *Do not open your booklets. There are some silent reading puzzles in these booklets. Some words are missing from sentences, and you have to write in the word that you think should go in each blank space. Let's do the first sample together.*

Work through the example paragraph aloud with the students. Read the first sentence, pausing for the blank, and have the students suggest an answer. Have them write the answer in the proper space. Repeat this process with the second sentence. Then have the students read the third sentence to themselves and fill in the answer. Check their work.

SAY: *In the paragraphs inside the booklet, write the one word in each blank that you think should go there. Just write one word in each blank space. If you can't think of a word, go on to the next one. When you come to the end of the first page, go straight to the second without waiting to be told, and continue until you come to the end.*

You have 15 minutes to complete the test. If you do finish before the time is up, look over your work. Don't worry about the correct spelling—this is not a spelling test. Try to spell each word as best you can.

After answering any questions, have students begin. After the time has expired or when students appear to have finished, ask students to stop.

This is not a strictly timed test. Students should be given a reasonable amount of time to complete the test. You may want to adjust the time limit if you are giving students fewer passages to complete.

▶ **WHAT IT MEANS** Use the scoring key that follows each form to correct the students' work. Place the total number of words correctly scored in the box after each passage. Then determine the total score and enter it on page 1 of the test booklet. Refer to the scoring criteria on the following page to determine approximate reading grade level. For those students whose reading comprehension is below their current grade level, additional assessments should be administered that evaluate specific reading comprehension skills.

Scoring Criteria **Elementary Level**

Score	Reading Grade Level
1–4	Grade 1 and below
5–8	Grade 2, Early
9–14	Grade 2, Late
15–20	Grade 3, Early
21–25	Grade 3, Late
26–30	Grade 4, Early
31–34	Grade 4, Late
35–38	Grade 5, Early
39–42	Grade 5, Late
43–46	Grade 6, Early
47–49	Grade 6, Late
50–56	Grade 7 and above

Scoring Criteria **Upper Level**

Score	Reading Grade Level
1–40	Administer Elementary Level
41–55	Grade 7 and above

▶ **WHAT'S NEXT?** Students who score below grade level will benefit from an assessment provided by the *Fry Oral Reading Test,* the *San Diego Quick Assessment of Reading Ability,* and the *Critchlow Verbal Language Scale* to determine if fluency, word recognition, or vocabulary deficits are the underlying causes of poor comprehension.

McLeod Assessment of Reading Comprehension, Elementary Level

Name________________________ Grade________ Date____________

DO NOT TURN OVER THE PAGE UNTIL YOU ARE TOLD.

Pat Has a Cold

Pat did ____________________ feel very well. Dad gave her ____________________ hot milk. She drank the milk and went to rest ____________________ her bed.

TOTAL SCORE

A Hungry Cat

Kitty jumped up and sat on the table. She watched the fish swim round ____________ round in the glass bowl. She tried ____________ push the bowl with ____________ paw, but could not tip ____________ over.

A Trip to the Hospital

Mike woke up in the middle of the night ____________ called out for his mother and father. He ____________ them that he was ____________ feeling well and that ____________ was a sharp pain ____________ his side. Wrapping him ____________ a blanket, Mike's parents rushed ____________ to the hospital. A ____________ examined him and informed his ____________ that an operation was necessary.

GO TO THE NEXT PAGE.

Scottie Raises the Alarm

Something seemed to be wrong with Scottie, the family dog, when she woke up suddenly late one winter evening. ____________________ air was filled with smoke, and flames ____________________ coming from the stove in the corner ____________________ the kitchen. She ran upstairs to where the family was sleeping and began ____________________ bark loudly. Suddenly, the lights were switched ____________________ in each bedroom and Scottie watched ____________________ waited until the family ____________________ gone downstairs. Then she followed them ____________________ of the house and into ____________________ cool night air.

A Modern Pirate

Carol had just finished reading a book about the pirates who used ____________________ sail the seven seas. She closed ____________________ eyes and soon she was asleep and dreaming ____________________ she was a pirate. She was not like the pirate in the book but one who flew ____________________ spaceship and attacked other spaceships. Instead ____________________ gold, silver, and diamonds, her booty included precious fuels ____________________ expensive computers.

GO TO THE NEXT PAGE.

Joshua

Each day Joshua woke at six in the morning. For most boys of his age, ____________________ to school was only a dream. Joshua himself had to ____________________ to provide money for the members ____________________ his family. Each day he had an hour's walk ____________________ the capital city where ____________________ would pick up a box containing plastic jewelry. For ____________________ next ten hours he ____________________ walk the streets, stopping tourists and begging them to buy some of the jewelry. The only ____________________ he rested was during the hottest part of the ____________________, when he was able to drink ____________________ tepid water and to ____________________ the orange that he had picked up at the market. At the ____________________ of the day he would receive the few coins that made up his pay, walk ____________________, eat a small supper, and then ____________________ asleep. He was always ____________________ tired to enjoy the normal life of a young boy.

☐

GO TO THE NEXT PAGE.

In the Valley of the Unknown Planet

Listen. Can you hear that whistling noise? It seems to be __________________ from that mountain. Kris and Michael volunteered to __________________ out and investigate. They put on their __________________ suits and grabbed their laser pistols. They __________________ the safety of their underground headquarters and began __________________ cross the empty terrain that lay before __________________. Without encountering any problems they reached __________________ mountain. Their bulky space suits __________________ climbing difficult but after a few hours __________________ reached the summit of the __________________. Before them stood a huge monument that __________________ been constructed by previous settlers. The whistling started __________________ and now the two spacemen __________________ the cause.

STOP. LOOK OVER YOUR WORK UNTIL TIME IS UP.

Scoring Key – Elementary Level

Correct responses for each passage are listed below. Mark errors in the test booklet. Do not count misspellings as an error. Count the number of correct responses and record this number in the space provided on the first page of the test booklet.

Pat Has a Cold

n't; not
some
in; on

A Hungry Cat

and
to
her
it

A Trip to the Hospital

and
told
not; n't
there
in
in
him
doctor
parents

Scottie Raises the Alarm

The; the
were
of
to
on
and
had
out
the

A Modern Pirate

to
her
that
a
of
and

Joshua

going
work
of
to
he
the

Joshua *(continued)*

would
time
day
some
eat
end
home
fall
too

In the Valley of the Unknown Planet

coming
go
space
left
to
them
the
made
they
mountain
had
again
knew

McLeod Assessment of Reading Comprehension, Upper Level

Name__________________ Grade____ Date__________

DO NOT TURN OVER THE PAGE UNTIL YOU ARE TOLD.

Pat Has a Cold

Pat did ______________ feel very well. Dad gave her ______________ hot milk. She drank the milk and went to rest ______________ her bed.

TOTAL SCORE

Mrs. Hill and Her Garden

Everyone on West Street knows Mrs. Hill.

______________ is the little old lady who lives ______________ the little white house.

All summer long ______________ is out working in her garden. This ______________ is what she likes to do best ______________ all.

"Hello, Mrs. Hill," her friends say ______________ they go by. "May we help you?"

Mrs. ______________ always says with a smile, "No, ______________ you." And she goes on working with ______________ many plants and flowers.

One day last month, Mrs. Hill looked around ______________ garden. She looked ______________ at the sky. "It is ______________ to take my house plants in," she ______________ "It will start to get cold soon."

______________ by one, Mrs. Hill took her plants ______________ the house.

GO TO THE NEXT PAGE.

The Enemy

In a corner of Mrs. Smith's living ________________ hangs a golden cage. The cage is ________________ home of Goldie, the parrot. Mrs. Smith also ________________ a very haughty cat who, come what may, ________________ be the master of the ________________.

For several days now the cat has noticed ________________ Mrs. Smith has been paying more ________________ to Goldie. She never stops saying: "What ________________ darling he is! How sweet he is! ________________ well he talks!"

The cat is fed ________________. He notices that it is easy for ________________ mistress to open the cage to feed ________________ bird. So he takes advantage of her absence and, by ________________ the cage door with ________________ paw, lets the bird escape.

☐

GO TO THE NEXT PAGE.

The Clever Crow

A thirsty crow found a water jug. Since there ________________ only a little water in ________________, she could not reach it with her ________________. She hopped back a few steps and ________________ flew against the jug. The jug did ________________ move from its place. The crow saw ________________ it was too heavy. But now she brought little stones ________________ the field and threw ________________ into the jug, so that the ________________ soon rose higher. At last she could dip ________________ beak into the water and quench her ________________.

☐

GO TO THE NEXT PAGE.

Once Upon a Time

Once upon a time there was a prisoner whom nobody ever ________________ to see, and to whom no friend ever came to say ________________ kind word in his dark ________________. He led a dreary, wretched life, but one ________________ a little mouse came out of a ________________ in the corner. As it was ____________ timid, it disappeared as soon as the ________________ moved, but soon it came back. ________________ threw it a crumb from his scanty meal. From then on the little mouse ________________ back to see him every day.

It ________________ to come and snuggle up against his neck or play on ________________ hands. To cut a long story ________________, they became real friends, and his dark ________________ never seemed as lonesome ________________ the prisoner when the little mouse ________________ there.

STOP. LOOK OVER YOUR WORK UNTIL TIME IS UP.

Scoring Key – Upper Level

Correct responses for each passage are listed below. Mark errors in the test booklet. Do not count misspellings as an error. Count the number of correct responses and record this number in the space provided on the first page of the test booklet.

Pat Has a Cold

n't; not
some
in; on

Mrs. Hill and Her Garden

she
in
she
work
of
as
Hill
thank
her
at
up
time
said
One
into

The Enemy

room
the
has
will
house
that
attention
a
How
up
his/the
the
opening
his

The Clever Crow

was
it
beak
then
not
that

The Clever Crow
(continued)

from
them
water
her
thirst

Once Upon a Time

came
a
cell
day
hole
very
prisoner
He
came
used
his
short
cell
to
was

K–8 Diagnostic
Assessment

Writing

- **Analytic and Timed Writing Assessments**
- **Individual Student Profile**
- **Class Information**
- **Student Self-Assessments**

Writing Assessments

ANALYTIC ASSESSMENTS

One kind of writing assessment is the analytic protocol. An analytic assessment can be used to score writing according to quantitative measures, such as fluency and conventions. Fluency is typically recorded as the average number of words produced per minute. A common way to assess maturity is by determining the average number of words per sentence. As Brown (1973) noted in his work in oral language, the length of the utterance (in his case orally) reflected developmental sophistication. In other words, the longer the utterance, the more likely the child is to be older or more linguistically developed. Conventions also can be assessed by determining the average number of errors per sentence. For instance, Fearn and Farnan (2001) suggest counting the number of mechanical errors—spelling, capitalization, and punctuation—and dividing that number by the number of sentences. Other analytic assessments can include the number of sentences written, the overall number of words written, and the average sentence length. Use the Student Profile on page 4 to record each student's scores. Use the Class Summary Information chart on page 5 to analyze your class needs. The Student Self-Assessment form on page 6 is provided to give you insights into how each student perceives the writing assignment.

TIMED WRITING ASSESSMENTS

Analytic assessment data is frequently coupled with a holistic or attribute assessment to gain a picture of a student's writing that is both quantitative and qualitative in nature. An excellent way to look at the progress of a group of students over time in both dimensions is via timed writing prompts. During the first weeks of school, and about every six weeks thereafter, collect timed writing samples for analytic and attribute assessment. Establish a time limit (usually between 20 and 45 minutes, depending on the grade level) and administer the prompt on the same date. The prompts should include various genres and be age- and grade-level-appropriate, for example:

- ***Describe your ideal bedroom.***
- ***Are school uniforms a good idea?***
- ***My goals for sixth grade are . . . .***

- ***Explain to a Martian how to make a peanut butter and jelly sandwich.***
- ***Was Marty a sneaky boy? (based on a class reading of* Shiloh*)***

Because they're timed, students have a common assessment experience across classrooms. These timed writing samples allow a grade level or a department to control for background knowledge while examining unedited, first-draft writing. After administering the assessment, students are asked to count the overall number of words and write it at the top of the first page. They also count the number of sentences in the piece. This is an important labor-saving step for teachers. The following steps are then employed:

1. The paper is first read for conventions. The number of errors in punctuation, capitalization, grammar, and spelling are recorded. This should be measured according to grade-level expectations.
2. The analytic portion of the assessment is then calculated, including: number of words written, average sentence length, and average number of errors per sentence.
3. Papers are then traded with other teachers to be scored using either a holistic or attribute rubric. Trade papers with one another in order to take advantage of a fresh perspective. Since you evaluate your own students' writing for an entire school year, this is as an opportunity for your students to write to a new reader.
4. The papers are returned to the classroom teacher for a second round of scoring. This phase of the process raises interesting and valuable questions among teachers about the attributes. For example, you might have a very interesting conversation at an English department meeting among your colleagues about what constitutes a good summary. These conversations are incredibly important for your own teaching practices.
5. Classroom teachers bring examples of scored student work to the next grade-level or department meeting. In particular, bring examples that show a range of mastery. The focus of the conversation is on how these inform your teaching.

Individual Student Assessment Profile

Name: ____________________ **Teacher:** ____________________

	MONTH 1	MONTH 2	MONTH 3	MONTH 4	MONTH 5	PLANS FOR NEXT SEMESTER
Analytic:						
Words per minute						
Words per sentence						
Errors per sentence						
Attributes:						
Ideas / Genre						
Organization and Focus						
Voice						
Word Choice						
Sentence Fluency / Structure						
Conventions						
Presentation						
Timed Writing Results						
Self-Assessment						
Conference Notes:						

Class Summary Information

Grade: ____________ School Year: ________ From: _____ To: _____

Student	Words per Minute (WPM)	Sentence Length	Errors per Sentence	Attributes Score	Holistic Score

Next steps for teaching: ______________________________

____

Student Self-Assessment

Name: ______________________________ Date: ______________

Title: ____

Please complete this and attach it to your assignment.

Yes	*No*		*Explain*
☐	☐	Did you understand the assignment?	______________
☐	☐	What was hard for you?	______________
☐	☐	What was easy for you?	______________
☐	☐	How did you help yourself?	______________
☐	☐	Is there anything you wished you had gotten help for?	______________
☐	☐	What do you think is the best feature of this piece?	______________

Circle the words you think your readers will use to describe your piece:

funny	fascinating	exciting
sad	confusing	boring
moving	touching	challenging
surprising	thought-provoking	inspiring
interesting	puzzling	humdrum